Kindergarten | Knowledge 8

Seasons and Weather

Teacher Guide

Amplify Core Knowledge Language Arts |
Core Knowledge®

ISBN 978-1-68161-011-5

Printed in the USA
BRN.2023.04

Contents

SEASONS AND WEATHER

Introduction

This introduction includes the necessary background information to be used in teaching the *Seasons and Weather* domain. The Teacher Guide for *Seasons and Weather* contains eight daily lessons, each of which is composed of two distinct parts, so that the lesson may be divided into smaller chunks of time and presented at different intervals during the day. Each entire lesson will require a total of sixty minutes.

This domain includes a Pausing Point following Lesson 5, after all four seasons have been introduced. At the end of the domain, a Domain Review, a Domain Assessment, and Culminating Activities are included to allow time to review, reinforce, assess, and remediate content knowledge. You should spend no more than fifteen days total on this domain.

DOMAIN COMPONENTS

Along with this Teacher Guide, you will need:

- Flip Book for *Seasons and Weather*, which can also be found at learning.amplify.com

- Image Cards for *Seasons and Weather*

- Activity Book for Domains 7–12

- Digital Components for *Seasons and Weather*

RECOMMENDED RESOURCES

You should consider various times throughout the day when you might infuse the curriculum with authentic domain-related literature. If you are able to do so, you may recommend students select books from the Recommended Resources list. In addition, if you recommend that caregivers read aloud with their student each night, you may wish to suggest that they choose titles from this list to reinforce the concepts covered in this unit.

You might also consider creating a classroom lending library, allowing students to borrow domain-related books to read at home with an adult. The Recommended Resources list, which also includes online resources, can be found online in the digital components for this domain at learning.amplify.com.

Core Knowledge Kindergarten Teacher Handbook, edited by E. D. Hirsch, Jr. and Souzanne A. Wright (Core Knowledge Foundation, 2004) ISBN 978-1890517694

WHY SEASONS AND WEATHER ARE IMPORTANT

This domain will introduce students to the concept of weather. Students will learn that different regions of Earth experience different weather patterns throughout the year. They will also learn that we can think about a year and the related weather patterns in terms of four seasons: winter, spring, summer, and autumn. Students will also learn why knowing about the weather is important, and how weather affects our daily lives and activities.

As the weather associated with each season varies depending upon where one lives, students throughout the United States will have different experiences with regard to the four seasons. There are, however, certain common seasonal features that will be true for all children living within the continental United States; for example, summer is always a warmer season, in general, than winter. The lessons and Read-Alouds included in this domain have been carefully written to make these common seasonal features clear, while still encouraging you to customize the discussions and subsequent activities to make students aware of the specific weather patterns in your area. Implicit in understanding the relationship between weather and seasons is having an understanding of time. Your students' grasp of the concepts discussed in this domain will be enhanced if they are already somewhat familiar with basic temporal concepts, such as day, week, month, and year. You will note that, within the lessons that follow, we recommend frequently referencing to a monthly calendar as a way of making the idea of time concrete.

The kinds of directed observations and hands-on activities associated with documenting the daily weather—such as looking at a thermometer, examining precipitation collected in a rain gauge, or observing the types of clouds in the sky—will help students more fully grasp the concepts they will hear about in this domain.

CORE CONTENT OBJECTIVES

Students will:

- Demonstrate understanding of the following units of time and their relationship to one another: day, week, month, year

- Name the four seasons in cyclical order, as experienced in the United States, and correctly name a few characteristics of each season

- Characterize winter as generally the coldest season, summer as generally the warmest season, and spring and autumn as transitional seasons

- Draw pictures that show an understanding of each season

- Characterize the North and South Poles as always cold in temperature, the middle section of the earth as usually warm, and most of the United States as having four seasons

- Describe daily weather conditions of their own locality in terms of temperature (hot, warm, cool, cold), cloud cover (sunny, cloudy), and precipitation (rain, snow, sleet)

- Name at least one month in a specific season while referring to a calendar

- Name at least one holiday in a specific season

- Describe any unique seasonal differences that are characteristic of their own locality (change of color and dropping of leaves in autumn; snow or ice in winter; increased rain, and/or flooding in spring, etc.)

- Identify ways in which weather affects daily routines, such as dress, activities, etc.

- Identify a thermometer as an instrument used to measure temperature and describe how it works

- Explain the lesson the grasshopper learns at the end of the fable, "The Grasshopper and the Ants"

- Identify characteristics of thunderstorms

- Describe safe and unsafe behaviors during thunderstorms

- Explain why weather prediction is important in daily life

CORE VOCABULARY FOR SEASONS AND WEATHER

The following list contains all of the core vocabulary words in *Seasons and Weather* in the forms in which they appear in the Read-Alouds or, in some instances, in the "Introducing the Read-Aloud" section at the beginning of the lesson. Boldfaced words in the list have an associated Word Work activity. The inclusion of the words on this list does not mean that students are immediately expected to be able to use all of these words on their own. However, through repeated exposure throughout the lessons, they should acquire a good understanding of most of these words and begin to use some of them in conversation.

Lesson 1 **characteristics** cycle patterns seasons weather	**Lesson 4** **distinct** indoors sunscreen thermometer	**Lesson 7** gear **severe** shelter strike
Lesson 2 blizzards cautiously freezing point **frigid** halt	**Lesson 5** chill **progresses**	**Lesson 8** meteorologist meteorology record satellites **warning**
Lesson 3 floods **gradually** thaw	**Lesson 6** future **last** shivering	

WRITING

In this domain, students will focus on using details to describe key concepts in informational texts about *Seasons and Weather*. Students will create a Weather Diary to observe, record, and predict the weather. They will also use drawing to identify important characteristics of the seasons, and they will complete a sequencing activity to illustrate the cycle of seasons. Students will also present a weather report at the end of the domain.

The following activities may be added to students' writing portfolios to showcase student writing within and across domains:

• Weather Diary (Lessons 1, 2, 3, 4, 7)

• Drawing and Sequencing the Seasons (Lessons 5, 6)

• any additional writing completed during the Pausing Point, Domain Review, or Culminating Activities

SEASONS AND WEATHER
What's the Weather Like?

Speaking and Listening

Students will discuss the purpose of a calendar and how to use it.
[SL.K.1]

Reading

Students will identify the four seasons and describe different types of weather.
[RI.K.3]

Language

Students will demonstrate an understanding of the Tier 2 word *characteristics*.
[L.K.5c]

Writing

With assistance, students will use drawing to describe characteristics of the
weather and make predictions about the weather in the future.
[W.K.2]

FORMATIVE ASSESSMENT

Activity Page 1.1

Weather Diary Students will use a drawing
activity to observe and predict the weather
[W.K.2]

LESSON AT A GLANCE

	Grouping	Time	Materials
Introducing the Read-Aloud			
Domain Introduction	Whole Group	10 min	❑ monthly calendar
Core Connections			❑ U.S. map
Read-Aloud			
Purpose for Listening	Whole Group	30 min	
"What's the Weather Like?"			
Comprehension Questions			
Word Work: *Characteristics*			
This is a good opportunity to take a break.			
Application			
Multiple Meaning Word Activity: *Seasons*	Whole Group Independent	20 min	❑ Poster 1M: Seasons
			❑ Activity Page 1.1
			❑ paper
Weather Diary			❑ stapler
			❑ drawing tools
Take-Home Material			
Caregiver Letter			❑ Activity Page 1.2

Introducing the Read-Aloud

- Prepare a monthly calendar for discussion. You may wish to display a calendar for the duration of this domain.

- Prepare a U.S. map for display during this domain.

  - If possible, color the North and South Poles blue. Color the area around the equator red, and color the rest of the map green.

- Prepare to locate Washington, D.C. on a map.

Notes to Teacher

This lesson assumes that students already have some experience using a monthly calendar. The discussion in Introducing the Read-Aloud constitutes a review of the basic units of time, such as day, week, month, and year. If students have had little or no prior experience with the use of a monthly calendar, it is strongly recommended that such a calendar be introduced and used on a daily basis as this domain is taught, in order to solidify students' knowledge of the basic units of time.

Application

- Prepare weather diaries (Activity Page 1.1) for each student. Collect them after use each day to ensure that students do not lose them.

- Prepare to take students on a "weather walk" each day, if possible.

- If possible, display a thermometer outside the school building so that you can read the temperature each day. If that isn't possible, refer to a weather website for daily temperatures.

- If possible, secure computer access for students to find out about the weather in other regions.

Universal Access

- Gather different books about weather to pass around the class. The school and local libraries may be good resources.

characteristics, n. ways we can describe and group people or things
Example: Two of Yesenia's characteristics are her curly hair and her kindness.
Variation(s): characteristic

cycle, n. events that happen over and over in the same order
Example: The cycle of the seasons happens every year and includes winter, spring, summer, and autumn.
Variation(s): cycles

patterns, n. things that repeat themselves over and over
Example: The pattern on her shirt was made up of green, red, and blue hearts.
Variation(s): pattern

seasons, n. the different times of the year—winter, spring, summer, and autumn
Example: My favorite seasons are spring and summer because the weather is warmer and there is more time to play outside.
Variation(s): season

weather, n. the temperature and other outside conditions at a particular time and place
Example: Tomorrow the weather will be cold and rainy.
Variation(s): none

Vocabulary Chart for "What's the Weather Like?"

Type	Tier 3 Domain-Specific Words	Tier 2 General Academic Words	Tier 1 Everyday Speech Words
Vocabulary	seasons	characteristics patterns weather	
Multiple Meaning		cycle	
Sayings and Phrases	cycle of the seasons pen pal		

Lesson 1: What's the Weather Like?

Introducing the Read-Aloud

Speaking and Listening: Students will discuss the purpose of a calendar and how to use it.

[SL.K.1]

DOMAIN INTRODUCTION (5 MIN)

- Briefly review different units of time as they relate to one another.

- Using a large monthly calendar, point to the current date and explain that today is one day.

- Then point to the entire week, Sunday through Saturday, explaining that this time period is called one week.

- Ask students to count the number of days in a week.

- Have one student point to each day on the calendar as the class chants the days of the week.

- Next, explain that all of the weeks shown on this single page of the calendar represent a time period called a month.

- Ask students to count the number of weeks in a month, pointing to the calendar.

- Explain that about four weeks make up a month, and twelve months make up a year.

- Now explain that within the twelve months, there are four different seasons.

- Remind students that they learned about the seasons in Domain 4, *Plants*, and Domain 5, *Farms*.

- Ask students to name the seasons.

- Explain that the seasons—winter, spring, summer, and autumn (or fall)— occur at different times of year.

- Help students match each season with the corresponding months on the calendar.

Support

Have students chant the days of the week with a partner.

Speaking and Listening

Exchanging Information and Ideas

Entering/Emerging
Reframe questions as simple yes/no questions (e.g.,"Have you ever received a letter in the mail?").

Transitioning/Expanding
Provide students with a specific sentence frame (e.g., "I received a letter in the mail from . . .").

Bridging
Encourage students to use key details in complete sentences (e.g., "I received a letter from my cousin in Alabama.").

Flip Book 1A-1

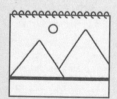

Challenge

Ask students to guess why someone who writes and exchanges letters might be called a "pen pal."

• Tell students that over the next couple of weeks, they are going to learn about the different seasons in a year.

CORE CONNECTIONS (5 MIN)

• Prepare students for the stylistic use of a pen pal as a narrator in this domain by using the following questions to prompt discussion:

  ◦ Do you ever get letters from a friend or relative who lives somewhere else?

  ◦ From whom do you get letters?

  ◦ Have you ever heard the words *pen pal*?

Explain that a pen pal is a friend with whom you exchange written letters but whom you may only see occasionally, if at all.

Show image 1A-1: Annie in Washington, D.C.

• Tell students that in the next several Read-Alouds they will be hearing letters from a pretend pen pal named Annie, who lives in Washington, D.C.

• Show students a map of the United States and point to Washington, D.C.

• Explain that Washington, D.C. is the capital of our country, the United States of America.

• Tell students that Washington, D.C. is where the president of our country lives and works.

• Have students look out the window and describe the weather.

• Next, point to the students' hometown on the map and discuss whether their hometown is near or far from where Annie lives.

• Explain that not everyone in the United States has the same weather on any given day.

• Explain that the weather where Annie lives may be very different right now from the weather in their hometown (unless they live in Washington, D.C., of course).

• Tell students that Annie's letters will tell them about the seasons and weather in her hometown of Washington, D.C.

Check for Understanding

One-Word Answer: How many days are there in a week? *(seven)*

How many months are there in a year? *(twelve)*

How many seasons are there? *(four)*

Is the weather the same all across the United States? *(no)*

Lesson 1: What's the Weather Like?
Read-Aloud

30M

Reading: Students will identify the four seasons and describe different types of weather.

[RI.K.3]

Language: Students will demonstrate an understanding of the Tier 2 word *characteristics*.

[L.K.5c]

PURPOSE FOR LISTENING

- Tell students to listen to learn the names of the four seasons of the year.

- Tell students to listen carefully to learn about different places on Earth that have different types of weather.

"WHAT'S THE WEATHER LIKE?" (15 MIN)

Support

Explain that the word *seasons* can have other meanings. The word *seasons* also means adds spice to food to give it more flavor.

Show image 1A-1: Annie in Washington, D.C.
Hello! My name is Annie, and I live in a big city called Washington, D.C. I'm in fifth grade, but I remember when I was in kindergarten, just like you. Right now in school, my class is learning about **seasons** and **weather**. *Seasons are different times of the year, and weather is the temperature and conditions outside.* For my school project, I'm going to be your weather pen pal. I'm going to teach you what the weather is like where I live. I will also tell you about the weather in different areas, or places, on Earth. You can help me with my project by answering all my questions, so I can learn about what the seasons and weather are like where you live.

Support

Tell students that when Annie says she will be their weather pen pal that means she will write letters to tell them about the weather in her hometown, Washington, D.C.

Show image 1A-2: Kinds of weather
There are many different kinds of weather. There is sunny weather, cloudy weather, windy weather, rainy weather, and stormy weather. What is the weather like outside today where you live?

My teacher says that no matter where you live on Earth, the weather is always changing, hour by hour, and day by day. *That means the weather never stays the same.* But even though the weather changes, there are still weather **patterns** during certain times of the year. *A pattern is something that repeats itself.* For example, the weather pattern in the summer is mostly sunny and warm. Weather patterns may change a lot in some places, and very little in other places. It all depends on where you live on Earth.

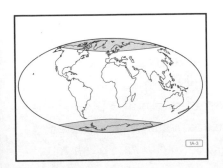

Show image 1A-3: Earth with northern and southern polar regions colored blue

This is a map of the earth. I've colored two areas on the map blue. *[Point to the blue areas of the map.] The color blue is often used to stand for things that are cold.* One is at the North Pole and one is at the South Pole. Even though the North and South Poles are at opposite ends of the earth from each other, they share the same weather patterns. The weather pattern at the North and South Poles is always cold, and the land is usually covered by ice.

Challenge

Ask students if they can describe any weather patterns that take place in your area.

Show image 1A-4: Antarctica

This is the South Pole, which is located on the continent of Antarctica. It is one of the coldest places on Earth. The ground is covered by ice all year long, though it almost never rains or snows here. The wind can be strong, and the temperature is freezing cold.

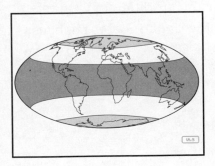

Show image 1A-5: Middle section of the earth colored red with blue polar regions

I've colored the middle area of this map red. *[Point to the red area of the map.] The color red is often used to stand for things that are hot.* The weather pattern in this area is usually very warm all year long. The biggest change in the weather during different times of the year is the amount of rain.

Show image 1A-6: Rainforest
During certain months in the rainforest, the day may start off warm and sunny, but by afternoon it may rain very, very hard. This weather pattern occurs almost every day! This area gets lots of rain and sun almost year-round. The rain and sun keep the plants and trees green and healthy.

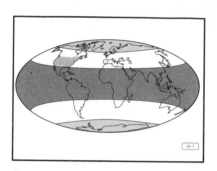

Show image 1A-7: The earth with colored areas and the United States in green
Do you see the part of this map that is colored green? This is most of the United States, the country where we live. *[Point to the United States on the image. You can also point to where Washington, D.C., is roughly located.]* Most of the United States is on the continent of North America, although the state of Hawaii is made up of islands located in the Pacific Ocean. In most of the United States, it's not always cold, like at the North and South Poles, and it's not always hot, like at the middle section of the earth. The weather in most of the United States changes with every season, so we get cold weather, hot weather, and everything in between.

Show image 1A-8: Seasons
There are four seasons in a year: *[Point to each image as you read the corresponding season.]* winter, spring, summer, and autumn. *Here, the word* seasons *means the different times of the year.* Each season has different weather, so the weather in the United States changes depending on where you live and which season it is. Plants, trees, grass, and flowers change in different seasons. You will also see different kinds of animals in different seasons.

Show image 1A-9: Winter

This image shows the season called winter. Winter is the coldest season. In some places, snow and ice cover the ground during wintertime. Other places that do not have snow and ice are still colder in winter than in other seasons. Some animals, like bears, sleep during the winter season.

Show image 1A-10: Spring

Eventually, winter ends and spring begins. *The word* eventually *means that something happened after some time has passed.* In spring, the sun shines a little longer and warmer each day, which melts the ice and snow. *The snow and ice turn to water as the sun's warmth gets stronger.* In spring, new leaves appear on the trees, new plants grow up from the warming earth, and flowers bloom again. Many baby animals are born during the spring, too!

Show image 1A-11: Summer

After spring comes summer. Summer is the hottest season of the year in the United States. Summer is the season in which all the plants are at their greenest—full of leaves, flowers, and fruit. Birds, bugs, and other animals are easiest to spot in the summer.

Show image 1A-12: Autumn

Finally, after summer comes autumn. Autumn is also called "fall." In most places in the United States, the leaves change colors and fall off certain types of trees in autumn. The air outside gets cooler and the sun shines a little less each day. Autumn is when farmers harvest their fruits and vegetables, birds fly south, and everyone gets ready for winter.

Show image 1A-13: Seasons diagram

Let's say the seasons together: winter, spring, summer, and autumn. Do you know what season it is right now where you live? How do you know? *[Pause for students to respond.]* Each season has its own special **characteristics**. *Characteristics are ways we can describe and group things. Each season has things that make it different from the others.* For example, a characteristic of summer is hot weather, and a characteristic of winter is snow.

The seasons are different depending on where you live. Not all places get snow in the winter, and not all places are steaming hot in the summer. But one thing is for sure: no matter where you live, the seasons always change in the same order, year after year.

When something happens over and over again in the same order, it's called a **cycle**. Every year the cycle of the seasons begins in winter, followed by spring, summer, autumn, and back to winter.

I'll be talking about my hometown, Washington, D.C., a lot in my letters, but the characteristics of the four seasons where you live might be a little different. It will be fun to see if your weather is different from mine!

I'll say good bye for now, but I will write again soon. Until then, I hope you are enjoying beautiful weather where you live!

Your friend,

Annie

Check for Understanding

Turn and Talk: What is the weather like in the South Pole? *(The weather is very cold, the land is covered by ice, there are glaciers in the surrounding water, and it rarely rains or snows.)*

What is the weather like in the rainforest? *(It is very warm most of the year, the amount of rain varies throughout the year, and there are rainforests there.)*

COMPREHENSION QUESTIONS (10 MIN)

Show image 1A-5: Middle section of the earth colored red with blue polar regions

1. **Literal** Which area on the map is always cold? *(It is always cold in the blue areas, which are called the North and South Poles.)* Which area on the map is usually warm? *(It is usually warm in the red area in the middle of the earth.)*

2. **Literal** Which season is the coldest? *(Winter is the coldest season.)* Which season is the hottest? *(Summer is the hottest season.)*

3. **Inferential** What are some characteristics of, or ways to describe, autumn? *(In the fall, the leaves are changing colors and falling off certain types of trees. It also starts to get a little colder outside.)*

4. **Inferential** What are some characteristics of, or ways to describe, spring? *(In the spring, it starts to get warmer outside. New leaves start to grow on trees, flowers bloom, and new plants grow.)*

5. **Evaluative** *Think Pair Share:* What were the most interesting facts you learned from the Read-Aloud today? What did the author say that made them more interesting to you? *(Answers may vary, but should include support from the Read-Aloud.)*

WORD WORK: CHARACTERISTICS (5 MIN)

1. In the Read-Aloud you heard, "Each season has its own special characteristics."

2. Say the word *characteristics* with me.

3. *Characteristics* are ways we can describe and group people and things.

4. Characteristics of summer in the United States include hot temperatures and a lot of sunshine.

5. Describe some characteristics of the person sitting next to you. Try to use the word *characteristics* when you describe your neighbor. [Ask two or three students. If necessary, guide and/or rephrase students' responses: "Some characteristics of _____ are . . ."]

6. What's the word we've been talking about?

7. Is *characteristics* a singular word or a plural word? *(plural)* How do you know? *(It ends with an 's'; it means more than one, etc.)* Can you think of other words that are plural? *(Answers may vary.)*

Use a Making Choices activity for follow-up. If any of the things I say are examples of the characteristics of a good friend, say, "That is a characteristic of a good friend." If they aren't characteristics of a good friend, say, "That is not a characteristic of a good friend."

- being a good listener *(That is a characteristic of a good friend.)*

- sharing *(That is a characteristic of a good friend.)*

- always wanting to do things their way *(That is not a characteristic of a good friend.)*

- being fun to play with *(That is a characteristic of a good friend.)*

Lesson 1: What's the Weather Like?
Application

Writing: With assistance, students will use drawing to describe characteristics of the weather and make predictions about the weather in the future. **[W.K.2]**

MULTIPLE MEANING WORD ACTIVITY: SEASONS (5 MIN)

Sentence in Context: Seasons
Show Poster 1M: Seasons

- Remind students that in the Read-Aloud they heard, "There are four seasons in a year: winter, spring, summer, and autumn."

- The word *seasons* is a plural word, meaning there is more than one. How many seasons are there? *(four)* What is the singular word for *seasons*, meaning only one? *(season)*

- Here, *seasons* mean the different times of the year.

- Have students hold up one or two fingers to indicate which image on the poster shows this meaning. *(1)*

- *Seasons* can also mean adds spice to food to give it more flavor.

- Have students hold up one or two fingers to indicate which image on the poster shows this meaning. *(2)*

- Have students turn to a neighbor and make a sentence for each meaning of *seasons*.

- Tell students to use complete sentences.

- Call on several students to share their sentences.

Flip Book Poster 1M

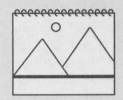

WEATHER DIARY (15 MIN)

- Discuss with students the current season and ask them what the weather has been like in your area the last few days.

- Tell students that they will keep a weather diary over the course of the next week to track the weather on a daily basis.

- Provide each student with a copy of Activity Page 1.1 and three pieces of paper in order to make a small weather diary, starting with today's date.

Activity Page 1.1

Speaking and Listening

Exchanging Information and Ideas

Entering/Emerging
Ask students yes/no questions about the weather and encourage them to ask their own questions about the weather.

Transitioning/Expanding
Encourage students to build on what the previous student has said about the weather.

Bridging
Challenge students to say something more about what the previous student has said about the weather.

Challenge

With assistance, have students use the internet or a local newspaper to research weather in Washington, D.C. and compare it to the weather in their hometown. If students live in Washington, D.C. or somewhere nearby, choose a location farther away to provide more contrast.

- If possible, take the class outdoors for a "weather walk" at the same time each day to discuss the day's weather and to make recordings in the weather diary.

- If it is not possible to go outside, observe the weather from a classroom window.

- Have students draw a simple picture of a sun, a sun with clouds, clouds, or clouds and rain depending on the weather each day.

- If you have an outside thermometer, you may also wish to have students write down the outside temperature, and/or have them draw a simple thermometer and color in how high or low the liquid in the thermometer is.

- Reinforce the concept of yesterday, today, and tomorrow by asking the following questions to prompt discussion:

  ◦ What is the weather like today?

  ◦ How is the weather today different from the weather yesterday?

  ◦ What do you think the weather will be like tomorrow?

- With assistance, have students use the internet to locate images and information for their weather diary.

- Collect the weather diaries to monitor progress. Be sure to return them to students for the next lessons.

End Lesson

Lesson 1: What's the Weather Like?
Take-Home Material

CAREGIVER LETTER

- Send home Activity Page 1.2.

SEASONS AND WEATHER
Winter

PRIMARY FOCUS OF LESSON

Speaking and Listening

Students will discuss the seasons and their corresponding months.
[SL.K.1]

Reading

Students will identify and describe characteristics of winter.
[RI.K.2]

Language

Students will demonstrate an understanding of the Tier 3 word *frigid*.
[L.K.5c]

Writing

With assistance, students will use drawing to describe characteristics of the
weather and make predictions about the weather in the future.
[W.K.2]

FORMATIVE ASSESSMENT

Activity Page 1.1

Weather Diary Students will use a drawing
activity to observe and predict the weather.
[W.K.2]

	Grouping	Time	Materials
Introducing the Read-Aloud			
What Have We Already Learned?	Whole Group	10 min	❑ calendar
Essential Background Information or Terms			
Read-Aloud			
Purpose for Listening	Whole Group	30 min	❑ thermometer
"Winter"			
Comprehension Questions			
Word Work: *Frigid*			
This is a good opportunity to take a break.			
Application			
Weather Diary	Independent	20 min	❑ Activity Page 1.1 ❑ drawing tools ❑ informational trade book about winter of teacher's choice

ADVANCE PREPARATION

Read-Aloud

- Bring in a thermometer for display.

Application

- Find an informational book about winter in your classroom or school library to read aloud.

- Return weather diaries to students.

- If possible, secure computer access for students to look for images for their weather diaries and to find out about the weather in other regions.

Universal Access

- There are a number of songs about the four seasons available on the Internet. You may choose to teach students one of these songs to help them remember the cycle of seasons. An option is the following song, sung to the tune of "Oh My Darling, Clementine":

  There are four seasons,
  There are four seasons,
  There are four seasons in the year.
  Winter, spring, then
  Summer and autumn.
  There are four seasons in the year.

- Gather different books about the weather around the world to pass around the class. The school or local libraries may be good resources.

blizzards, n. heavy snowstorms with a lot of wind and snow
Example: Blizzards hit much of the country at the same time.
Variation(s): blizzard

cautiously, adv. carefully
Example: I cautiously looked for cars in both directions before I crossed the street.
Variation(s): none

freezing point, n. the temperature at which a liquid will turn into a solid
Example: Water turns to ice at its freezing point of 32 degrees Fahrenheit.
Variation(s): freezing points

frigid, adj. very cold
Example: The frigid temperature outside makes me want to stay inside where it's warm.
Variation(s): none

halt, n. a stop
Example: The traffic light was not working, so the policeman held up his hand when he wanted to bring the traffic to a halt.
Variation(s): halts

Vocabulary Chart for "Winter"			
Type	Tier 3 Domain-Specific Words	Tier 2 General Academic Words	Tier 1 Everyday Speech Words
Vocabulary	blizzards freezing point frigid	cautiously halt	
Multiple Meaning			
Sayings and Phrases	freezing point		

Lesson 2: Winter

Introducing the Read-Aloud

Speaking and Listening: Students will identify the seasons and their corresponding months.

[SL.K.1]

WHAT HAVE WE ALREADY LEARNED? (5 MIN)

- Review with students that different parts of the earth experience different types of weather.

- Also remind them that, in most of the United States, there are four seasons and that each season has distinct characteristics, or qualities, that describe them.

- Have students identify in proper sequence the four seasons of the year as experienced in most of the United States: winter, spring, summer, and autumn.

- Discuss with students what they learned about winter in the last Read-Aloud.

- Ask students how winter is different from the other seasons. *(It is the coldest season, and some areas of the United States have snow and ice in winter.)*

- Remind students that in the first Read-Aloud in this domain, they learned that some animals seek shelter from the cold in winter, much like people do.

- Many animals also hibernate, or sleep, during the winter season.

ESSENTIAL BACKGROUND INFORMATION OR TERMS (5 MIN)

- Tell students that in the next Read-Aloud, they will hear about the first season in the cycle of the seasons—winter.

- Show students the monthly calendar and assist them in identifying today's month and date.

- Explain that in the United States, the season of winter begins in the month of December and includes the months of January and February. Flip to these pages in the calendar.

Speaking and Listening

Exchanging Information and Ideas

Entering/Emerging
Ask students yes/no questions about the similarities and differences between the seasons.

Transitioning/Expanding
Encourage students to build on what the previous student has said about the similarities and differences between the seasons.

Bridging
Challenge students to say something more about what the previous student has said about the similarities and differences between seasons.

Challenge

Discuss with students that the seasons are reversed in the Southern Hemisphere. For example, in Australia, summer is December, January, and February.

Support

Have the class chant each month and corresponding season.

- Remind students of the current date, especially the month, and ask if they are presently in the winter season.

- Tell students that you will need their help during the Read-Aloud.

- Demonstrate a shivering motion for students.

- Tell them that you would like them to repeat this shivering motion whenever they hear the word *winter* in the Read-Aloud.

- As you explore each season and the holidays that are celebrated, document students' learning of the holidays with a graph. Use the graphs to explore and capture more information about each holiday. You can return to the graph at the end of Lesson 5. Consider having students create a poster or flyer at home of their family's favorite holiday, using the information collected during this activity, and share with classmates.

Check for Understanding

Recall: What are the four seasons? *(The four seasons are winter, spring, summer, and autumn.)*

What season is it now? *(Answers will vary.)*

Lesson 2: Winter
Read-Aloud

30M

Reading: Students will identify and describe characteristics of winter.
[RI.K.2]

Language: Students will demonstrate an understanding of the Tier 3 word *frigid*.
[L.K.5c]

PURPOSE FOR LISTENING

• Tell students that today they will listen to a new letter from their pen pal, Annie, about the season of winter.

• Explain that the main topic, or the main idea, of today's lesson is winter.

• Tell students to listen carefully so they can identify characteristics of, or ways to describe, winter.

"WINTER" (15 MIN)

Show image 2A-1: Annie in winter
Dear Kindergartners,

Hi from your pen pal, Annie! In my last letter, I told you about the four seasons that occur in many parts of the United States—winter, spring, summer, and autumn. Today I'm going to tell you about winter. What kinds of things do you think of when I say winter? Snowmen?

Icicles? I'll tell you what I think of: cold! *[Demonstrate a shivering motion for students and prompt them to repeat the motion whenever they hear the word winter.]*

Winter is the coldest season of the year in most of the United States. The shortest day of the year is on December 21. *It's called the shortest day of the year because it is the day with the least amount of daylight.* It marks the beginning of winter. Winter also includes the months of January and February.

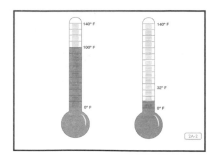

Show image 2A-2: Thermometers

It can get very cold in the winter in most of the United States. We can tell just how cold it is by using a tool called a thermometer. A thermometer measures temperature, which is a number we use to talk about how hot or cold it is. When it is hot outside, the liquid in the thermometer rises towards the top. When it is cold outside, the liquid in the thermometer stays down near the bottom. *[Show students an actual thermometer, then talk about the thermometers in the image.] Is it hot or cold when the liquid rises up in the thermometer? Is it hot or cold when the liquid stays low down in the thermometer? Think of "warm up" and "cool down" to help you remember. Which thermometer shows what the temperature might be like in the winter?*

Show image 2A-3: Winter clothing

Another way that you can tell it is wintertime is by the way people are dressed. What are the people in the picture wearing that helps them stay warm in the winter? *[Pause for students' responses.]* Winter clothing is made to protect you from the cold and to keep your body nice and warm while you spend time outside. Hats, mittens, and scarves help you stay warm in the winter.

Show image 2A-4: Snowy Washington, D.C.

It is usually cold during the winter where I live in Washington, D.C. Sometimes it even gets cold enough to snow! I wish it would snow every day, but the temperature must fall below freezing—below 32 degrees Fahrenheit—in order for it to snow. If the air between the clouds and the ground is below the **freezing point**, then, instead of rain, snowflakes will probably fall. *Remember, the freezing point is the temperature at which a liquid turns into a solid, or rain turns into snow and ice.*

Support

Explain that the word *point* can have other meanings. The word *point* also means to show someone something by moving your finger in a particular direction.

Some years, Washington, D.C., gets heavy snowstorms known as **blizzards** that bring city traffic to a halt *or to a stop* and force the schools to close. *Blizzards are snowstorms with lots of snow and lots of wind. They make it difficult for people to walk and drive.* There are other years when it only snows once or twice. This means that some winters are colder and snowier than others in Washington, D.C. What is it like during the winter where you live? Does it ever snow?

Show image 2A-5: Shoveling snow
When it snows, everyone works together to clear the snow. People use snow shovels to shovel snow off walkways so that others do not slip and get hurt.

Show image 2A-6: Snowplow
In many places where it snows, snowplows get to work clearing the streets. The big plow on the front of the truck scrapes the snow and ice from the streets. These trucks also carry salt or other chemicals, which they spread on the roads as they pass. *Have you ever seen a truck like this before? [Pause for responses.]* The salt and chemicals melt the remaining ice and keep new ice from forming, which makes the roads safer for people to drive their cars.

People should always drive and walk slowly and **cautiously**, or carefully, in the snow. Snow and ice are slippery, and whether you are walking or driving, you should use extra caution when the ground is covered with snow or ice.

Show image 2A-7: Snowman
I always cheer up when it starts to snow because I love to play in the snow. I like to build snowmen and have snowball fights with my friends.

Challenge

Have students think of other examples of times to do something cautiously.

Show image 2A-8: Sledding

Another way to have fun in the snow is to go sledding! After a big snow, all you need is a nice steep hill, warm clothes, and something to ride on to go sledding.

Show image 2A-9: Fireside

After playing or working outside in the winter, it is always nice to come back inside to get warm again. Some homes have fireplaces, where people light logs on fire to help warm the house. I love reading a good book by the warm fire.

In places where it stays really cold in the winter, people also use gas furnaces and electric heaters to help keep the air inside their homes nice and warm. Of course, having a few extra blankets on the bed is always a good idea on those **frigid** *or very cold* winter nights.

Show image 2A-10: Christmas, Hanukkah, and Kwanzaa

Winter is also a time when some people from different religions celebrate holidays. Christmas, a Christian holiday, comes on December 25. Hanukkah, a Jewish holiday, also falls around this time, as does Kwanzaa, a week-long holiday celebrated by some African Americans. *What winter holidays does your family celebrate?*

To celebrate these and other holidays in wintertime, sometimes people string colorful lights around their homes and neighborhoods. You should see Washington, D.C., during the holiday season: all of the lights make it a magical place.

Show image 2A-11: New Year's Eve

Another important winter holiday falls on December 31, which is the last day of the year. This day is called New Year's Eve. January 1, the day after December 31, marks the beginning of a new year. January 1 is called New Year's Day. On New Year's Day, many people make resolutions, or lists of things they would like to do better in the new year.

Show image 2A-12: Chinese New Year

Luck and good fortune are common themes for the Lunar New Year, also known as Chinese New Year, which is a holiday that falls around the end of January and beginning of February. The color red, thought to be a sign of good fortune and happiness, is the color chosen to wear during the festivities. Homes are decorated with red paper cut into designs, and happy wishes written on red paper are also hung throughout the house. Children often receive red envelopes with money tucked inside; the people who receive these envelopes are also supposed to receive good fortune in the New Year. Feasting on fish, pork, poultry, tangerines, oranges, dumplings, and special cakes, families gather to wish each other good luck.

There are so many fun things to do during the winter! What's your favorite part of winter? [Pause for student responses.]

Your friend,

Annie

Check for Understanding

Point and Say It: When I point to the month on the calendar and say its name, you say the season that occurs during that month. (January/Winter, etc.)

Speaking and Listening

Exchanging Information and Ideas

Entering/Emerging
Reframe questions as simple yes/no questions (e.g.,"Do you wear a coat in winter?").

Transitioning/Expanding
Provide students with a specific sentence frame (e.g., "In winter, I wear . . .").

Bridging
Encourage students to use key details in complete sentences (e.g., "In winter, I wear a warm coat and woolen mittens to keep warm.").

COMPREHENSION QUESTIONS (10 MIN)

Show Image 2A-2: Thermometers

1. **Literal** When it is cold outside, is the liquid in the thermometer close to the top or close to the bottom? *(When it is cold outside, the liquid in the thermometer is close to the bottom.)*

2. **Inferential** What are some characteristics of winter? *(Some characteristics of winter are that it is very cold and can snow.)*

3. **Inferential** How do you dress for winter? *(During winter, I wear a hat, a coat, a scarf, and mittens.)*

4. **Inferential** What happens to rain when the temperature drops below the freezing point? *(When the temperature drops below the freezing point, rain may turn into snow or ice.)*

5. **Evaluative** Name some good things and some bad things about lots of snow falling. *(Some good things about lots of snow falling are that I can play, build snowmen, and go sledding in the snow. Some bad things about lots of snow falling are that people need to drive and walk cautiously, and sometimes they can't walk or drive at all.)*

WORD WORK: FRIGID (5 MIN)

1. In the Read-Aloud you heard, "Of course, having a few extra blankets on the bed is always a good idea on those frigid winter nights."

2. Say the word *frigid* with me.

3. *Frigid* means very cold.

4. My hands were frigid because I was playing outside in the snow without gloves!

5. Tell about a time when the weather felt frigid. Try to use the word *frigid* when you tell about it. [Ask two or three students. If necessary, guide and/or rephrase students' responses: "The weather felt frigid when . . ."]

6. What's the word we've been talking about?

Use an Antonyms activity for follow-up. The opposite of *frigid* is very hot. If any of the things I describe sound like they are frigid, say, "_____ is frigid." If any of the things I describe sound like they are very hot, say, "_____ is very hot."

- the temperature during a blizzard (*The temperature during a blizzard is frigid.*)

- a boiling pot of water (*A boiling pot of water is very hot.*)

- the way your nose feels when you are outside in the snow (*The way your nose feels when you are outside in the snow is frigid.*)

- a typical summer afternoon (*A typical summer afternoon is very hot.*)

- popsicles in the freezer (*Popsicles in the freezer are frigid.*)

Lesson 2: Winter
Application

Writing: With assistance, students will use drawing to describe characteristics of the weather and make predictions about the weather in the future. **[W.K.2]**

WEATHER DIARY (20 MIN)

- Show students the informational book about winter you selected to read.

- Ask students to identify the front cover of the book. Ask students what kinds of things are on the front cover of a book. (*Answers may vary, including title, author, illustrator, pictures, etc.*)

- Ask students to identify the back cover of the book. Ask students what kinds of things are on the back cover of the book. (*Answers may vary, depending on the book.*)

- Ask students where the title page is usually found in a book. Then, show students the title page and discuss what can be found on the page.

- Read the book or part of the book to students, leaving enough time for the Weather Diary activity.

- Return Activity Page 1.1 to students and have them turn to the second page.

- If possible, take students outdoors for a "weather walk" at the same time each day to discuss the day's weather and to make recordings in their weather diaries.

- If it is not possible to go outside, observe the weather from a classroom window.

- Have students draw a simple picture of a sun, a sun with clouds, clouds, or clouds and rain depending on the weather each day.

- If you have an outside thermometer, you may also wish to have students write down the outside temperature, and/or have them draw a simple thermometer and color in how high or low the liquid in the thermometer is.

- Have students compare the weather observed yesterday and today.

Activity Page 1.1

Support

Have students work in pairs to decide what to draw.

Challenge

Have students label their diary entries describing the weather they observed.

- Use the following questions to promote discussion:
  - What is the weather like today?
  - How is the weather today different from the weather yesterday?
  - What do you think the weather will be like tomorrow?

- With assistance, have students use the internet to locate images and information for their weather diary.

- With assistance, have students use the internet to see what winter is like in other locations such as California, Russia, India, China, and Australia.

- Have them record the average temperature, snowfall, rain, etc.

- If the students do not have access to the internet, have them use books you collected about weather around the world.

- Collect the weather diaries to monitor progress. Be sure to return them to students for the next lessons.

End Lesson

Speaking and Listening

Exchanging Information and Ideas

Entering/Emerging
Ask students yes/no questions about the weather and encourage them to ask their own questions about the weather.

Transitioning/Expanding
Encourage students to build on what the previous student has said about the weather.

Bridging
Challenge students to say something more about what the previous student has said about the weather.

3

SEASONS AND WEATHER
Spring

Speaking and Listening

Students will recall characteristics of winter and identify the calendar months that correspond to spring.
[SL.K.2]

Reading

Students will identify and describe characteristics of spring.
[RI.K.2]

Language

Students will demonstrate an understanding of the Tier 2 word *gradually*.
[L.K.5c]

Writing

With assistance, students will use drawing to describe characteristics of the weather and make predictions about the weather in the future.
[W.K.2]

FORMATIVE ASSESSMENT

Activity Page 1.1

Weather Diary Students will use a drawing activity to observe and predict the weather.
[W.K.2]

	Grouping	Time	Materials
Introducing the Read-Aloud			
What Have We Already Learned?	Whole Group	10 min	❏ calendar
Essential Background Information or Terms			
Read-Aloud			
Purpose for Listening	Whole Group	30 min	
"Spring"			
Comprehension Questions			
Word Work: *Gradually*			
This is a good opportunity to take a break.			
Application			
Sayings and Phrases: April showers bring May flowers	Whole Group Independent	20 min	❏ Activity Page 1.1 ❏ drawing tools ❏ informational trade book about spring
Weather Diary			

ADVANCE PREPARATION

Application

- Find an informational trade book about spring in your classroom or school library to read aloud.

- If possible, secure computer access for students to find images and information for their weather diaries.

Universal Access

- Gather different books about weather to pass around the class. The school and local libraries may be good resources. Be sure to highlight books with diverse character representation and authorship.

• Bring in a bouquet of flowers for students to pass around and smell.

Note: Be sure to check your school's policy regarding plant/flower distribution and allergies

CORE VOCABULARY

floods, v. when a body of water overflows and spreads out onto dry land
Example: The river floods when we get too much rain at once.
Variation(s): flood, flooded, flooding

gradually, adv. slowly; bit by bit
Example: The fields across from our home gradually turn green in the spring.
Variation(s): none

thaw, v. to melt or soften after being frozen
Example: I can't wait for the ground to thaw so I can plant my flowers.
Variation(s): thaws, thawed, thawing

Vocabulary Chart for "Spring"			
Type	**Tier 3** **Domain-Specific Words**	**Tier 2** **General Academic Words**	**Tier 1** **Everyday Speech Words**
Vocabulary		gradually thaw	
Multiple Meaning		floods	
Sayings and Phrases	April showers bring May flowers In like a lion and out like a lamb		

Lesson 3: Spring

Introducing the Read-Aloud

Speaking and Listening: Students will recall characteristics of winter and identify the calendar months that correspond to spring.
[SL.K.2]

WHAT HAVE WE ALREADY LEARNED? (5 MIN)

- Review with students that different parts of the earth experience different types of weather.

- Remind them that, in most of the United States, there are four seasons and that each season has distinct characteristics.

- Tell students that, so far, they have learned about winter, one of the four seasons.

- Ask the following questions about winter to prompt discussion:
  - What is the weather like in winter?
  - What type of clothing do you wear in winter?
  - What kinds of foods do you eat in winter?
  - What kinds of activities do you like to do in winter?

- Review the specific information that students have already learned about winter, noting any unique characteristics of winter in your locality.

Speaking and Listening

Exchanging Information and Ideas

Entering/Emerging
Reframe questions as simple yes/no questions (e.g.,"Do you wear a coat in winter?").

Transitioning/Expanding
Provide students with a specific sentence frame (e.g., "In winter, I wear . . .").

Bridging
Encourage students to use key details in complete sentences (e.g., "In winter, I wear a warm coat and woolen mittens to keep warm.").

Challenge

Have a student point to the months on the calendar that correspond to spring.

Support

Have the class chant each month and corresponding season.

ESSENTIAL BACKGROUND INFORMATION OR TERMS (5 MIN)

- Explain to students that after winter, the next season in the cycle is spring.

- Show students the monthly calendar, and assist them in identifying today's month and date.

- Explain that in the United States, the season of spring begins in the month of March and includes the months of April and May, flipping to these pages in the calendar.

- Remind students of the current date, especially the month, and ask if they are presently in the spring season. (**Note:** Do not expect students to identify the current season if it is neither winter nor spring.)

- Tell students that you will need their help during the Read-Aloud. Whenever students hear the word *spring* in the Read-Aloud, they should hold up their hands like they are holding flowers and pretend to smell them.

Check for Understanding

Stand Up/Sit Down: There are four seasons. *(stand up)*

Spring comes after summer. *(sit down)*

Spring happens in March, April, and May. *(stand up)*

Read-Aloud

Reading: Students will identify and describe characteristics of spring.
[RI.K.2]

Language: Students will demonstrate an understanding of the Tier 2 word *gradually*.
[L.K.5c]

PURPOSE FOR LISTENING

- Tell students that the main topic, or main idea, of today's lesson is spring.

- Tell students that they will hear another letter from their pen pal, telling them about the season of spring in Washington, D.C.

- Tell them to listen carefully to find out about the different characteristics of spring.

"SPRING" (15 MIN)

Show image 3A-1: Spring months

Dear Kindergartners,

After winter, the next season is <u>spring</u>! *Here, spring means the time of the year when flowers bloom. Don't forget to sniff your flower when you hear the word* spring! Spring arrives **gradually**, bit by bit, beginning in mid-March, and it continues through the months of April and May. The air warms and the ground begins to **thaw** *The snow and ice begin to melt, or thaw, and the ground is no longer hard and frozen.* because the days are longer and there is more sunlight. The rivers and streams fill with water from all of the melted snow and ice. Tiny green leaves appear on some tree branches. A few new plants may also start to peek up out of the soil here and there. Hibernating animals wake up from their winter sleep. *Did you know that some animals like bears sleep most of the time during winter? They hibernate during winter when it's cold and wake up when it becomes warmer in spring.* These are all signs that spring has sprung! *Spring is here!*

Support

The word *spring* can have other meanings. The word *spring* also means a source of water coming up from the ground.

Spring is a very windy season. Some people say, "March comes in like a lion and goes out like a lamb." This means that the weather in spring changes from being stormy and windy *with the strength and power of a lion* in the beginning to calmer and milder by the end *like a soft, gentle lamb.* In fact, the windy beginning of spring is a perfect time to fly a kite!

Show image 3A-2: Spring showers

In addition to wind, there are also many rainy days in the early spring, particularly in March and April. I love when I get to wear my raincoat and rain boots because then I can splash in puddles! Sometimes after a spring rain shower you can see a colorful rainbow in the sky.

There is another old saying that tells us, "April showers bring May flowers." This means that the rains of April help flowering plants to grow big and healthy, so they produce beautiful, fragrant flowers in May and throughout the summer.

Show image 3A-3: Washington, D.C. cherry blossoms

The world outside truly changes during spring. Flowers are one of the most important signs of spring because they tell you that the plant world has come to life once again. *[Remind students to pretend to sniff a flower whenever they hear the word spring.]* Soon, bees will be buzzing among the flowers, birds will be chirping in the leafy trees, and the afternoon hours will be warm and pleasant.

Washington, D.C., is famous for the cherry blossoms that bloom here each spring. *[Point to the blossoms in the image.]* In April, the cherry trees throughout the city burst into bloom, and millions of brilliant pink and white flowers show that spring is here. My parents and I have a special spring picnic every year under the cherry blossoms.

Show image 3A-4: Farmers in spring

Spring is an important time on farms. *[Remind students that they learned about farms with Old MacDonald in the Farms domain.]* For the farmer, it is time to get back out in the fields. The farmer must plow his soil and prepare it for planting. He plows the field in order to stir up the soil's nutrients—that's food for plants— and loosen the ground so that new seeds will be able to take root. When the time is right, the farmer will go through his plowed fields and plant his seeds in neat rows. A couple of weeks later, the field will be brimming with little green seedlings, *or young plants* and by summer you won't be able to see the brown soil at all beneath all the big, green plants.

Show image 3A-5: Collage of farm animals

Spring is also an important time for the animals on the farm. Many animals give birth to new baby animals in the springtime. The barnyard and fields are full of baby animals, whose mothers nurse and care for them as they grow. Baby horses, called foals, frolic in the fields, lambs nuzzle close to the mother sheep, and ducklings line up and follow their mother duck to the pond.

Show image 3A-6: Potomac River

Washington, D.C., was built along the <u>banks</u> of the Potomac River. *Banks are the land alongside a river.* Rivers usually reach their highest levels during the spring. Melted snow from the surrounding fields and mountains drains into creeks and seeps through the ground to reach the river, where it will eventually flow out to the sea. Sometimes the river water becomes so high, it **floods**. *or overflows its banks*

Challenge

Ask students if they can think of any other meanings for the word *banks. (Students may respond that people keep their money in banks.)*

Show image 3A-7: Easter, Passover, and Holi

Several holidays are celebrated during the springtime. On the Christian holiday of Easter, people often go on Easter egg hunts to look for decorated eggs or an Easter basket full of candy. During the Jewish holiday of Passover, special food is served to family and friends at the Passover Seder. The Hindu holiday of Holi is a festival of colors, during which people celebrate the colors of springtime by dancing, singing, and sprinkling colored water on each other. *What holidays does your family celebrate in spring?*

Show image 3A-8: Iwo Jima Memorial

Another important holiday, called Memorial Day, is celebrated on the last Monday in May. On this day, we honor the American men and women who have fought and died in different wars to protect the United States. Many people also celebrate Memorial Day with parades, picnics, barbecues, and family gatherings. In Washington, D.C., we have a big concert to celebrate.

Show image 3A-9: Seasons diagram

[Point to each season and name them in order.]
What is spring like where you live? Is it any different from spring in Washington, D.C.?

Your friend,

Annie

Check for Understanding

Turn and Talk: With a partner, discuss the last questions in the read aloud:

What is spring like where you live?

Is it any different from spring in Washington, D.C.?

COMPREHENSION QUESTIONS (10 MIN)

1. **Literal** Name the months of spring. *(The months of spring are March, April, and May.)*

2. **Inferential** Describe some of the changes that happen from winter to spring. *(Some of the changes that happen from winter to spring are that the air warms, the ground thaws, and plants begin to grow again.)*

3. **Inferential** Why does the author say that spring is an important time on the farm? *(Spring is an important time on farms because it is the time when farmers need to start planting their new crops and baby animals are born.)*

4. **Evaluative** *Think Pair Share:* What activities can you do in spring that you can't do in winter? *(Answers may vary, but should include support from the Read-Aloud.)*

Support

If students have difficulty responding to questions, reread pertinent lines of the Read-Aloud and/or refer to specific images.

Speaking and Listening

Exchanging Information and Ideas

Entering/Emerging
Ask students yes/no questions about the activities they can do in spring but not in winter.

Transitioning/Expanding
Encourage students to build on what the previous student has said about the activities they can do in spring but not in winter.

Bridging
Challenge students to say something more about what the previous student has said about activities they can do in spring but not in winter.

WORD WORK: GRADUALLY (5 MIN)

1. In the Read-Aloud you heard, "Spring arrives gradually, bit by bit, beginning in mid-March, and it continues through the months of April and May."

2. Say the word *gradually* with me.

3. *Gradually* means slowly, or bit by bit.

4. If something happens gradually, it happens slowly. Snow melts gradually when it is very cold outside.

5. Tell about something that happens gradually. Try to use the word *gradually* when you tell about it. [Ask two or three students. If necessary, guide and/or rephrase students' responses: "One thing that happens gradually is _____."]

6. What's the word we've been talking about?

Use an Antonyms activity for follow-up. The opposite of *gradually* is *quickly*. If any of the things I describe happen gradually, say, "_____ happens gradually." If any of the things I describe happen quickly, say, "_____ happens quickly."

- the snow melting during spring (*The snow melting during the spring happens gradually.*)

- an ice cube melting in a cup of hot water (*An ice cube melting in a cup of hot water happens quickly.*)

- pulling your hand away from a hot stove (*Pulling your hand away from a hot stove happens quickly.*)

- a seedling growing into a full-sized plant (*A seedling growing into a full-sized plant happens gradually.*)

- a baby becoming a kindergartner (*A baby becoming a kindergartner happens gradually.*)

Lesson 3: Spring
Application

Writing: With assistance, students will use drawing to describe characteristics of the weather and make predictions about the weather in the future.
[W.K.2]

SAYINGS AND PHRASES (5 MIN)

April Showers Bring May Flowers

- Remind students that, in the Read-Aloud they just heard, Annie told them about an old saying, "April showers bring May flowers."

- The saying means that the rains in April will help flowering plants grow big and strong so that they produce beautiful May flowers.

- Explain that there is figurative meaning, or deeper meaning, behind the words of this saying.

- Tell students that this saying can also mean that if you are going through unhappy times, those unhappy times may lead to happier ones.

- This saying reminds people to have patience to get through the rain, or sad times. Eventually, the flowers, or happier times, will bloom.

- Tell students that if they ever go through unhappy times, they should think of the saying, "April showers bring May flowers," to remind them that happier times will come.

- Ask students to think of something good that happened after an unhappy time.

- Have students give examples using the saying.

Speaking and Listening

Offering Opinions

Entering/Emerging
Provide students sentence frames using a small set of learned phrases (e.g., "An example of an unhappy time followed by a happy time was . . .").

Transitioning/Expanding
Provide students sentence frames using an expanded set of learned phrases (e.g., "An example of an unhappy time followed by a happy time was . . .").

Bridging
Provide minimal support and guidance for open responses.

WEATHER DIARY (15 MIN)

- Show students the informational book about spring you selected to read.

- Ask students to identify the front cover of the book. Ask students what kinds of things are on the front cover of a book. (*Answers may vary, including title, author, illustrator, pictures, etc.*)

- Ask students to identify the back cover of the book. Ask students what kinds of things are on the back cover of the book. (*Answers may vary, depending on the book.*)

- Ask students where the title page is usually found in a book. Then, show students the title page and discuss what can be found on the page.

- Read the book or part of the book to students, leaving enough time for the Weather Diary activity.

- Return Activity Page 1.1 to students and have them turn to the third page.

- If possible, take the class outdoors for a "weather walk" at the same time each day to discuss the day's weather and to make recordings in the weather diary.

- If it is not possible to go outside, observe the weather from a classroom window.

- Have students draw a simple picture of a sun, a sun with clouds, clouds, or clouds and rain depending on the weather each day.

- If you have an outside thermometer, you may also wish to have students write down the outside temperature, and/or have them draw a simple thermometer and color in how high or low the liquid in the thermometer is.

- Have students compare the weather observed yesterday and today.
  - What is the weather like today?
  - How is the weather today different from the weather yesterday?
  - What do you think the weather will be like tomorrow?

- With assistance, have students use the internet to locate images and information for their weather journal.

- With assistance, have students use the internet to see what spring is like in other locations such as California, Russia, India, China, and Australia.

- Have them record the average temperature, snowfall, rain, etc.

- If the students do not have access to the internet, have them use books you collected about weather around the world.

- Help students identify any patterns that may have occurred.

- Collect the weather diaries to monitor progress.

End Lesson

Activity Page 1.1

Support

Have students work in pairs to decide what to draw.

Challenge

Have students label their diary entries with words, phrases, and sentences describing the weather they observed.

SEASONS AND WEATHER
Summer

PRIMARY FOCUS OF LESSON

Speaking and Listening

Students will compare and contrast the characteristics of winter and spring, and they will identify the calendar months that correspond to summer.
[SL.K.1]

Reading

Students will identify and describe the characteristics of summer.
[RI.K.2]

Language

Students will demonstrate an understanding of the Tier 2 word *distinct*.
[L.K.5c]

Writing

With assistance, students will use a drawing activity to describe current weather and identify weather patterns.
[W.K.2]

FORMATIVE ASSESSMENT

Activity Page 1.1

Weather Diary Students will use a drawing activity to record current weather and identify weather patterns.
[W.K.2]

Writing Studio

If you are using Writing Studio, you may begin Unit 4 Lesson 1 after completing this Knowledge lesson. If you have not done so already, you may wish to review the Writing Studio materials and their connections to this domain.)

LESSON AT A GLANCE

	Grouping	Time	Materials
Introducing the Read-Aloud			
What Have We Already Learned?	Whole Group	10 min	❏ calendar
Essential Background Information or Terms			
Read-Aloud			
Purpose for Listening	Whole Group	30 min	
"Summer"			
Comprehension Questions			
Word Work: *Distinct*			
This is a good opportunity to take a break.			
Application			
Weather Diary	Independent	20 min	❏ Activity Page 1.1 ❏ drawing tools ❏ informational trade book about summer of teacher's choice

ADVANCE PREPARATION

Read-Aloud

- Bring in a thermometer for display.

Application

- Find an informational book in your classroom or school library about summer to read aloud. Be sure to highlight books with diverse character representation and authorship.

- Return weather diaries to students.

- If possible, secure computer access for students to find images and information for their weather diaries.

Universal Access

- This domain presents a wonderful opportunity to learn about the holidays of different cultures, particularly the holidays celebrated by the students in your class. As you present the holidays for specific seasons, be sure to highlight holidays that your students celebrate during that season. Holding a cultural holiday celebration might be an interesting and informative activity for your class.

- Gather different books about weather around the world to pass around the class. The school and local libraries may be good resources.

CORE VOCABULARY

distinct, adj. clearly different
Example: The twins look alike, but they have distinct personalities.
Variation(s): none

indoors, adv. inside a building
Example: The hot weather makes me want to stay indoors where it's cool.
Variation(s): none

sunscreen, n. a lotion or spray that protects the skin from the sun
Example: When I go to the beach, I wear sunscreen so I don't get sunburned.
Variation(s): sunscreens

thermometer, n. a tool that measures temperature
Example: The thermometer outside says that the temperature is 75 degrees Fahrenheit.
Variation(s): thermometers

	Vocabulary Chart for "Summer"		
Type	**Tier 3** **Domain-Specific Words**	**Tier 2** **General Academic Words**	**Tier 1** **Everyday Speech Words**
Vocabulary	sunscreen thermometer (termómetro)	distinct (distinto) indoors	
Multiple Meaning			
Sayings and Phrases	Fourth of July stay indoors		

Lesson 4: Summer

Introducing the Read-Aloud

Support

Have the class chant each month and corresponding season.

Speaking and Listening: Students will compare and contrast the characteristics of winter and spring, and they will identify the calendar months that correspond to summer.

[SL.K.2]

Speaking and Listening

Exchanging Information and Ideas

Entering/Emerging
Ask students yes/no questions about the similarities and differences between the seasons.

Transitioning/Expanding
Encourage students to build on what the previous student has said about the similarities and differences between the seasons.

Bridging
Challenge students to say something more about what the previous student has said about the similarities and differences between the seasons.

WHAT HAVE WE ALREADY LEARNED? (5 MIN)

- Review with students that different parts of the earth experience different types of weather.

- Have students identify in proper sequence the four seasons in most of the United States.

- Tell students that, so far, they have learned about two of the four seasons, winter and spring.

- Review the specific information they have already learned about winter and spring, noting any unique characteristics in your locality.

- Ask students to compare the characteristics of winter and spring, using the following questions to prompt discussion:

  ◦ What are some similarities between winter and spring? (*Answers may vary, but should include that they both last three months.*)

  ◦ What are some differences between winter and spring? (*Answers may vary but should include support from the previous Read-Alouds.*)

  ◦ How does the clothing you wear differ in winter and spring? (*Answers may vary but should include support from the previous Read-Alouds.*)

  ◦ What activities can you do in winter but not in spring? (*Answers may vary but should include support from the previous Read-Alouds.*)

  ◦ What kinds of activities can you do in spring but not in winter? (*Answers may vary but should include support from the previous Read-Alouds.*)

ESSENTIAL BACKGROUND INFORMATION OR TERMS (5 MIN)

- Tell students that in the next Read-Aloud they will hear about the summer season.

- Show students the monthly calendar and assist them in identifying today's month and date.

- Explain that in most of the United States, the season of summer begins in the month of June and includes the months of July and August, flipping to these pages in the calendar.

- Remind students of the current date, especially the month, and ask if they are presently in the summer season. (**Note:** Do not expect the students to identify the current season if it is autumn, the one season they have yet to study.)

- Tell students that you will need their help during the Read-Aloud. Whenever students hear the word *summer* in the Read-Aloud, they should pretend to shield their eyes from the sun or pretend they are swimming.

Check for Understanding

Making Choices: Does spring follow winter or summer? *(winter)*

Would you pick flowers in winter or spring? *(spring)*

Is it winter or spring in April? *(spring)*

Is it winter or summer in February? *(winter)*

Is it spring or summer in July? *(summer)*

Challenge

Have a student point to the months on the calendar that correspond to spring.

Lesson 4: Summer

Read-Aloud

Reading: Students will identify and describe the characteristics of summer. **[SL.K.2]**

Language: Students will demonstrate an understanding of the Tier 2 word *distinct*. **[L.K.5c]**

PURPOSE FOR LISTENING

- Tell students the main topic, or main idea, of today's lesson is summer.

- Ask students to listen carefully to learn about different characteristics of summer.

"SUMMER" (15 MIN)

Show image 4A-1: Seasons

[Point to the picture for each season, and have students say which season it is.]

Dear Kindergartners,

Hi from your pen pal, Annie! Today I'm going to tell you about summer. What kinds of things do you think of when I say *summer*? [*Prompt students to pretend to shield their eyes from the sun or pretend to swim whenever they hear the word* summer.]

Support

Discuss with students why the days are longer in the summer. Explain that because the Earth is tilted on its axis, it is actually a little closer to the sun during the summer months. This means that we have more hours of daylight during summer because of the Earth's position as it orbits the sun.

Show image 4A-2: Summer months

My favorite season of the year is definitely summer because I love the warm weather and sunshine. Summertime means vacation because I don't have school during the summer months.

At the beginning of summer, our part of the earth receives the most sunlight that it will get all year long. The days are the longest they will be all year in the summer. In most of the United States, the summer season begins in the month of June and includes the months of July and August. No matter where you live in the United States, summertime will bring the warmest weather of the year.

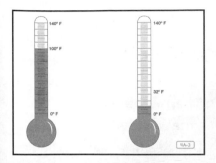

Show image 4A-3: Thermometers

One way to tell how warm it is outside is to look at a **thermometer**. *[Have students say the word* thermometer *together.]* Remember that a thermometer is a tool that measures the temperature. When it is cool outside, the liquid in the thermometer stays down in the lower part of the thermometer. When it is warm outside, the liquid rises in the thermometer and comes close to the top. Which thermometer do you think shows what the temperature might be like in the summertime? *[Pause and have students say whether the first or second thermometer shows a likely summertime temperature.]*

Show image 4A-4: Summer clothes

Do you remember that when we talked about the winter months, we said you could also tell how cold it was by the way people dress? The same is true in summer. You can tell how warm it is by the way people are dressed. All of these people are dressed for warm weather. What do you notice about the way they are dressed? *[Pause for students to respond.]*

Show image 4A-5: Washington Monument

As I've told you before, I live in Washington, D.C., the capital of the United States. My teacher says that Washington, D.C., is a good city to learn about when studying the seasons because here the four seasons are **distinct** *or clearly different* from one another. It's easy to tell by walking outside or looking out the window whether it is winter, spring, summer, or autumn.

Show image 4A-6: Summer in the city

Summer is the busiest time of year in Washington, D.C., because each year millions of Americans come to visit the famous monuments, museums, and buildings during their summer vacations. The city gets really crowded during the summer, but I like to see all the different kinds of people downtown.

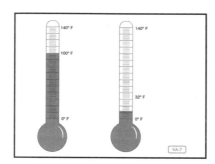

Show image 4A-7: Thermometers

During the summer, the weather can be very hot in Washington, D.C. See how high the liquid is in this thermometer to the left? It says it is 100 degrees Fahrenheit; that means it is really hot outside! It is a good thing there are so many vendors who sell cold refreshments, like ice cream and snow cones, to help visitors cool off!

Show image 4A-8: Mowing the grass

The trees in Washington, D.C. are full of green leaves during the summer. In my neighborhood, there are lots of parks with grassy areas that are mowed so people can enjoy them. On weekends, many of my neighbors are out working in their flower beds and gardens.

Show image 4A-9: Crowded pool

I like to go to the local swimming pool to keep cool in the summer, and lots of other people have the same idea. *[Remind students of the motion they should do when they hear the word summer.]* Everyone at the pool is wearing plenty of **sunscreen** so they do not get sunburned. *Sunscreen protects your skin from the sun and prevents sunburn.* Nothing ruins summer fun like a bad sunburn!

Show image 4A-10: Shady tree in the park
Sometimes you can rest under shady trees to protect yourself from the hot sun. Other people simply stay **indoors**, *or inside a cool building* especially on the hottest days.

Show image 4A-11: Fourth of July fireworks
The Fourth of July is the biggest summer holiday, and it is an especially important day in Washington, D.C. The Fourth of July is the birthday of the United States, and many people celebrate the day with family and friends. Lots of my friends have picnics or barbecues and take trips to the beach. I like to go to the parades during the day on the Fourth of July and then to the booming, colorful fireworks at night. I also love eating lots of watermelon!

Thanks to the Fourth of July and trips to the pool and beach, I always think of fun times when I think about summer. What is it like during the summer where you live?

Your friend,

Annie

Check for Understanding

Turn and Talk: With a partner, discuss Annie's question at the end of her letter: What is it like during the summer where you live? *(Answers may vary but should include support from the read-aloud.)*

Challenge

Ask students to describe other ways they can protect themselves from the sun and heat during the summer. *(Answers may vary, but may include wearing a swim shirt, drinking lots of water, and playing in the shade.)*

COMPREHENSION QUESTIONS (10 MIN)

<table><tr><td>

Support

If students have difficulty responding to questions, reread pertinent lines of the Read-Aloud and/or refer to specific images.

Speaking and Listening

Exchanging Information and Ideas

Entering/Emerging
Ask students yes/no questions about the activities they can do in summer but not in winter.

Transitioning/Expanding
Encourage students to build on what the previous student has said about the activities they can do in summer.

Bridging
Challenge students to say something more about what the previous student has said about activities they can do in summer.

</td></tr></table>

1. **Literal** Name the summer months. (*The summer months are June, July, and August.*)

Show image 4A-3: Thermometers

2. **Literal** What do thermometers do? (*Thermometers tell us how hot or cold it is.*)

   ◦ **Inferential** When it is hot outside, is the liquid in the thermometer closer to the top or closer to the bottom? (*When it is hot outside, the liquid in the thermometer is closer to the top.*)

3. **Inferential** Does the daylight on summer days last longer than on winter days? (*The daylight on summer days lasts longer than on winter days.*)

4. **Inferential** How is the way you dress on a hot summer day different from the way you dress for winter? (*During summer, I would wear shorts, a T-shirt, and flip-flops, but in winter I would wear a coat, a scarf, and mittens.*)

5. **Evaluative** *Think Pair Share:* What activities can you do in summer that you can't do in winter? (*Answers may vary.*)

WORD WORK: DISTINCT (5 MIN)

1. In the Read-Aloud you heard, "My teacher says that Washington, D.C., is actually a good city to learn about when studying the seasons because here the four seasons are distinct from one another."

2. Say the word *distinct* with me.

3. *Distinct* means clearly different.

4. Someone might notice the distinct smell of roses in a flower shop, meaning that the smell of roses stands out from the smells of the other flowers.

5. Tell about something that makes you distinct from your classmates. Try to use the word *distinct* when you tell about what makes you different. [Ask two or three students. If necessary, guide and/or rephrase students' responses: "One thing that makes me distinct is . . ."]

6. What's the word we've been talking about?

Use a Discussion activity for follow-up. Discuss the characteristics that make winter, spring, and summer distinct seasons. Be sure to begin your responses with "Characteristics that make _____ a distinct season are . . .".

Lesson 4: Summer
Application

Writing: With assistance, students will use a drawing activity to describe current weather and identify weather patterns.
[W.K.2]

WEATHER DIARY (20 MIN)

- Show students the informational book about summer you selected to read.

- Ask students to identify the front cover of the book. Ask students what kinds of things are on the front cover of a book. (*Answers may vary, including title, author, illustrator, pictures, etc.*)

- Ask students to identify the back cover of the book. Ask students what kinds of things are on the back cover of the book. (*Answers may vary, depending on the book.*)

- Ask students where the title page is usually found in a book. Then, show students the title page and discuss what can be found on the page.

- Read the book or part of the book to students, leaving enough time for the Weather Diary activity.

- Return Activity Page 1.1 to students and have them turn to the fourth page.

- If possible, take students outdoors for a "weather walk" at the same time each day to discuss the day's weather and to make recordings in their weather diaries.

- If it is not possible to go outside, observe the weather from a classroom window.

- Have students draw a simple picture of a sun, a sun with clouds, clouds, or clouds and rain depending on the weather each day.

- If you have an outside thermometer, you may also wish to have students write down the outside temperature, and/or have them draw a simple thermometer and color in how high or low the liquid in the thermometer is.

- Have students compare the weather observed yesterday and today.
  - What is the weather like today?
  - How is the weather today different from the weather yesterday?
  - What do you think the weather will be like tomorrow?

Activity Page 1.1

Support

Have students work in pairs to decide what to draw.

Challenge

Have students label their diary entries with words, phrases, and sentences describing the weather they observed.

- With assistance, have students use the internet to locate images and information for their weather journal.

- With assistance, have students use the internet to see what summer is like in other locations such as Texas, Alaska, Maine, Ecuador, Australia, Japan, and India.

- Have them report on the average temperature, snowfall, rain, etc.

- If students do not have access to the internet, have them use books you collected about weather around the world.

- After students have completed four entries, discuss the characteristics of the current season in your locality as well as the weather changes and temperature changes that occurred.

- Help students identify any patterns that may have occurred.

- Collect the weather diaries to monitor progress. Be sure to return them to students for the next lessons.

~~~~~~~~~~~~~~~~ End Lesson ~~~~~~~~~~~~~~~~

SEASONS AND WEATHER

Autumn

PRIMARY FOCUS OF LESSON

Speaking and Listening

Students will compare and contrast the characteristics of winter, spring, and summer, and they will identify the calendar months that correspond to fall.
[SL.K.1]

Reading

Students will identify and describe characteristics of autumn.
[RI.K.2]

Language

Students will demonstrate an understanding of the Tier 2 word *progresses*.
[L.K.5c]

Writing

Students will use a drawing activity to describe the four seasons.
[W.K.2]

FORMATIVE ASSESSMENT

Exit Pass

My Four Seasons Students will draw four pictures to describe each of the seasons.
[W.K.2]

	Grouping	Time	Materials
Introducing the Read-Aloud			
What Have We Already Learned?	Whole Group	10 min	❑ calendar
Essential Background Information or Terms			
Read-Aloud			
Purpose for Listening	Whole Group	30 min	
"Autumn"			
Comprehension Questions			
Word Work: *Progresses*			
This is a good opportunity to take a break.			
Application			
Multiple Meaning Word Activity: *Fall*	Whole Group Independent	20 min	❑ Poster 4M: Fall
			❑ paper folded into quarters
My Four Seasons Drawing Activity			❑ drawing tools
			❑ informational trade book about autumn of teacher's choice
Take-Home Material			
Caregiver Letter			❑ Activity Page 5.1

Application

- Find an informational book about autumn in your classroom or school library to read aloud.

- Prepare to divide students into pairs for the Multiple Meaning Word activity.

Universal Access

- Consider bringing in a collection of leaves to use as you talk about how the colors change during autumn.

- Gather different books about autumn to pass around the class. The school and local libraries may be good resources.

- Bring in various items that represent the four seasons. Items might include woolen gloves, hot chocolate packet, ice scraper, umbrella, plant seeds, flowers, sunscreen, goggles, beach towel, pumpkin, Halloween costume, and leaves. Have students sort the items based on the season they represent.

CORE VOCABULARY

chill, n. a cold sensation
Example: In the evening there was a chill in the air, and I was glad I had brought a sweater with me.
Variation(s): chills

progresses, v. moves forward or continues
Example: The students learn more and more as the school year progresses.
Variation(s): progress, progressed, progressing

	Vocabulary Chart for "Autumn"		
Type	**Tier 3** **Domain-Specific Words**	**Tier 2** **General Academic Words**	**Tier 1** **Everyday Speech Words**
Vocabulary	chill	progresses (progresa)	
Multiple Meaning			
Sayings and Phrases	Thanksgiving Day		

Lesson 5: Autumn

Introducing the Read-Aloud

Speaking and Listening: Students will compare and contrast the characteristics of winter, spring, and summer, and they will identify the calendar months that correspond to autumn.

[SL.K.1]

- Review with students that different parts of the earth experience different types of weather.

- Have students identify in proper sequence the four seasons of the year that are distinctly experienced in the United States.

- Tell students that, so far, they have learned about three of the four seasons: winter, spring, and summer.

- Review the specific information they have already learned about winter, spring, and summer, noting any unique characteristics in your locality.

- Use the following questions to prompt discussion:

  ◦ What are some of the characteristics of summer? (*Summer is usually hot and takes place in June, July, and August in the United States*)

  ◦ What do you wear in the summer? (*In most places, people wear light clothing like shorts and flip flops in the summer.*)

  ◦ What activities do you do during summer? (*Answers may vary but should include support from the Read-Aloud.*)

  ◦ How are spring and summer similar? How are they different? (*Answers may vary but may include that spring and summer are both three months long, are the warmest seasons, and are times when we wear cooler clothing.*)

  ◦ How are spring and summer different from winter? (*Answers may vary, but may include that winter is colder than spring and summer and that plants typically don't bloom in the winter.*)

- Tell students that today's Read-Aloud is called "Autumn."

- Show the students the monthly calendar and assist them in identifying today's month and date.

- Explain that in the United States, the season of autumn, also called fall, begins in the month of September and includes the months of October and November, flipping to these pages in the calendar.

- Remind students of the current date, especially the month, and ask if they are presently in the autumn season. (**Note:** Since you have now discussed the months included in all the seasons, the students may be able to identify the current season.)

- Tell students that you will need their help during the Read-Aloud. Whenever students hear the word *autumn* in the Read-Aloud, they should use their hands to demonstrate the motion of the falling leaves.

Check for Understanding

Recall: Name the four seasons in order starting with the coldest one. *(winter, spring, summer, and autumn.)*

In the United States when does autumn occur? *(Autumn occurs in September, October, and November.)*

In Australia, or the southern hemisphere, what season occurs in December? *(In the southern hemisphere, summer occurs in December.)*

In the United States, which season comes before autumn? *(Summer comes before autumn.)*

In the United States, which season comes after autumn? *(Winter comes after autumn.)*

Lesson 5: Autumn
Read-Aloud

30M

Reading: Students will identify and describe characteristics of autumn.
[RI.K.2]

Language: Students will demonstrate an understanding of the Tier 2 word *progresses*.
[L.K.5c]

PURPOSE FOR LISTENING

- Tell students that the main topic, or main idea, of today's Read-Aloud is autumn.

- Ask students to listen to find out about how the weather changes from summer to autumn.

- Tell them to listen carefully for details about the activities people do during autumn.

"AUTUMN" (15 MIN)

Show image 5A-1: Autumn months
What clue in the picture tells you it is autumn?

Dear Kindergartners,

Eventually the warm weather of summer ends and autumn begins. *[Prompt students to use their hands to demonstrate leaves falling whenever they hear the word* autumn *in the Read-Aloud.]* Kids are back in school in autumn. Autumn officially starts in the middle of September, and includes the months of October and November.

By autumn, the air becomes cooler than it was during the scorching, or very hot, summer months. It might still feel warm on some early autumn days, but there's a slight **chill** *or cold sensation* in the air at night. And by the end of autumn, it can be really cold during the day and at night!

Show image 5A-2: Deciduous tree
As autumn **progresses**, *or moves forward* the days get shorter and shorter. The sun rises just a little bit later and sets just a little bit earlier each day. By October in Washington, D.C., many of the trees' leaves don't look so green anymore. *[Review with students deciduous and evergreen trees from the* Plants *domain. Remind students that deciduous trees lose their leaves in the fall.]*

Show image 5A-3: Blue Ridge in autumn
During autumn, most of the leaves on the trees turn from green to bright yellow, orange, red, or brown. It's so beautiful! Last autumn, my family took a trip to the mountains near Washington, D.C., to enjoy the colors. The air was so cool and crisp, and we had a great time. Look at this picture from our trip: the forests as far as the eye can see are bright with fiery color!

Show image 5A-4: Raking leaves
Within a few weeks after the leaves of many trees turn different colors, deciduous trees begin to shed, or lose, their leaves. That's why another name for *autumn* is *fall*, because autumn is when the leaves of deciduous trees fall to the ground. *Remember that evergreen trees stay green all year round, while deciduous trees lose their leaves in the autumn.* The grass is soon covered with a blanket of brown leaves.

Do the leaves change color and <u>fall</u> off the trees where you live? If they do, you can do the same thing the kids in my neighborhood do: we rake up all the leaves into one enormous pile and then jump in it, just for fun. The leaves make a soft, crunchy cushion.

Challenge

Ask students why some parts of the country do not experience brightly colored leaves in autumn. *(Some areas of the country, like Texas, do not have many deciduous trees.)*

Support

Tell students the word *fall* has multiple meanings. The word *fall* can mean the season of autumn or when something drops down.

Show image 5A-5: Harvest time in the fields

If you travel for a few hours outside Washington, D.C., you will start to see farms. Autumn means harvest time for farmers. *Harvest time is when farmers gather their crops.* It's hard work being a farmer. All summer, farmers have been caring for their plants while they grow—watering them and making sure the weeds and bugs of summer do not ruin them. Autumn is the time to gather the fruits and vegetables in the fields.

When they've harvested their crops, the farmers all get together for a really fun event: the county fair. My family goes every year to the nearest county fair, and it is incredible. The farmers all bring their best vegetables and animals to show off how good they are at growing vegetables and raising farm animals.

Show image 5A-6: Pumpkins at the county fair

I took this picture of the pumpkins at last year's county fair. The fair's judges had already come by and judged them. Which pumpkins do you think the judges liked best? How do you know?

Show image 5A-7: County fair rides and booths

I wouldn't get so excited about the fair if it were only about vegetables! There are lots of fun rides and all kinds of foods, from cotton candy to corn dogs. Some people also take their chances playing games to win stuffed animals. Once, I won a gigantic teddy bear.

Show image 5A-8: Fall in the city

By early November, the air outside gets chilly in Washington, D.C. Sometimes the skies are clear and sunny, while other days are gray and cloudy. The wind blows more than it did during the summer. The autumn wind sends dry, crunchy leaves whirling and twirling through the streets and parks, and whispers that winter is coming soon!

Show image 5A-9: Thanksgiving dinner

In late November—as the autumn season is gradually winding to a close—comes one of the most important holidays in the United States: Thanksgiving Day. On this day, people in the United States like to gather with their families and friends. In my family, my grandparents and cousins and uncles and aunts from all over travel to have Thanksgiving dinner together. I always look forward to a grand feast of turkey, stuffing, potatoes, rolls, and cranberry sauce—with pumpkin pie for dessert. Then, my cousins and I play football in the yard! *[Tell students that they will learn more about the first Thanksgiving in the next domain.]*

Show image 5A-10: Bare trees

Thanksgiving is very close to the end of autumn in Washington, D.C. By that time, the trees are bare, the leaves are raked, and the air starts to feel very cold, especially at night. Once the trees look like this, you know that autumn is nearing an end, and that it will soon be winter. We are once again at the beginning of the cycle of the seasons!

Show image 5A-11: Seasons diagram
[Point to each season and name them in order.]

Now we've talked about every season and their different characteristics. What will I tell you about next? You'll just have to wait and see!

Your friend,

Annie

Check for Understanding

Turn and Talk: What are some of the holidays celebrated in autumn? What do you do on these holidays? Do you have any special traditions?

COMPREHENSION QUESTIONS (10 MIN)

1. **Inferential** What is the main topic, or main idea, of today's lesson? *(The main topic of today's lesson is autumn.)*

2. **Literal** Name the months of autumn. *(The months of autumn are September, October, and November.)*

3. **Inferential** What changes do you notice as summer progresses to autumn? *(As summer progresses to autumn, the weather becomes cooler, days are shorter, and trees change color and shed their leaves.)*

4. **Literal** Name a holiday that takes place during the autumn season. *(Answers may vary, but may include Thanksgiving or Halloween.)*

5. **Evaluative** *Think Pair Share:* Which season is your favorite season of the year? Why is it your favorite? *(Answers may vary.)*

Support

If students have difficulty responding to questions, reread pertinent lines of the Read-Aloud and/or refer to specific images.

Speaking and Listening

Exchanging Information and Ideas

Entering/Emerging
Ask students yes/no questions about their favorite season.

Transitioning/Expanding
Encourage students to build on what the previous students have said about their favorite season.

Bridging
Challenge students to say something more about what the previous students have said about their favorite season.

WORD WORK: PROGRESSES (5 MIN)

1. In the Read-Aloud you heard, "As autumn progresses, the days get shorter and shorter."

2. Say the word *progresses* with me.

3. *Progresses* means moves forward or continues. As something progresses, it usually changes. Things can progress over time, like when a person who progresses in age slowly gets older.

4. As the school year progresses, I learn more and more.

5. As winter progresses, it gets colder and colder. Tell about something that progresses, or moves forward. Try to use the word *progresses* when you tell about it. [Ask two or three students. If necessary, guide and/or rephrase students' responses: "Something that progresses quickly is _____." Or "Something that progresses slowly is _____."]

6. The word *progresses* has the word *progress* in it. *Progress* means to move forward. Tell students to listen to this word: *progressed.* Ask students what they hear at the end of the word. (students should say they hear the -*ed* ending, but they will most likely say 'd'.) Tell students that when action words or verbs end with the -*ed* sound, it means that it has already happened or happened in the past. Give other examples of verbs with -*ed* endings, such as walked, talked, jumped, etc. Have students give their own examples.

Use a Making Choices activity for follow-up. If any of the things I name move forward and change, say, "_____ progresses." If any of the things I name do not progress, say, "_____ stops." (Students may have different responses. If so, you may ask them to explain their responses.)

- the autumn season from September to November (*The autumn season from September to November progresses.*)

- the amount of knowledge you learn from year to year (*The amount of knowledge you learn from year to year progresses.*)

- when someone slams a door (*When someone slams a door, it stops.*)

- when someone pushes on the brakes in a car (*When someone pushes on the brakes in a car, it stops.*)

- a baby crawling and then learning how to walk (*A baby crawling and then learning how to walk progresses.*)

Lesson 5: Autumn

Application

Writing: Students will use a drawing activity to describe the four seasons. [W.K.2]

MULTIPLE MEANING WORD ACTIVITY: FALL (5 MIN)

Definition Detective
Show Poster 4M: Fall

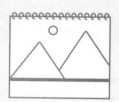

Flip Book Poster 4M

- Tell students that in the Read-Aloud they heard, "That's why another name for autumn is fall, because autumn is when the leaves of deciduous trees fall to the ground."

- Ask students to work in pairs to think of as many meanings for fall or ways they can use the word *fall* as possible.

- Have students hold up one or two fingers to indicate which image on the poster shows how the word *fall* is used in the lesson. *(1)*

- Explain that *fall* can also mean other things. *Fall* can mean to drop from a higher place to a lower place. *(2)*

- Have students hold up one or two fingers to indicate which image on the poster shows this meaning.

- Tell students to quiz their neighbor on the different meanings of *fall*. For example they could say, "I love how the trees change colors in the fall." Tell students their neighbor should hold up one finger to indicate that this meaning of *fall* matches the first picture.

MY FOUR SEASONS DRAWING ACTIVITY (15 MIN)

- Show students the informational book about autumn you selected to read.

- Ask students to identify the front cover of the book. Ask students what kinds of things are on the front cover of a book. *(Answers may vary, including title, author, illustrator, pictures, etc.)*

- Ask students to identify the back cover of the book. Ask students what kinds of things are on the back cover of the book. *(Answers may vary, depending on the book.)*

- Ask students where the title page is usually found in a book. Then, show students the title page and discuss what can be found on the page.

- Read the book or part of the book to students, leaving enough time for the Weather Diary activity.

- Tell students they have now learned about all four seasons and their characteristics.

- Refer to the images in today's Read-Aloud as needed.

- Tell students they are going to draw items that represent each of the four seasons.

- Give each student a piece of paper that has been folded into quarters. Starting in the upper left-hand corner and moving clockwise, have students draw items that represent winter, spring, summer, and autumn.

- Have students include colors, plants, animals, and clothing they would see during each season.

- After they have finished drawing, have students present their illustrations to a partner and explain the characteristics of each season.

~~~ End Lesson ~~~

Lesson: 5 Autumn

Take-Home Material

<span style="background:black;color:white">**CAREGIVER LETTER**</span>

- Send home Activity Page 5.1.

Support

If students have trouble thinking of what to draw, you may wish to show them images from the Read-Aloud.

Challenge

Have students include a word, phrase, or sentence that describes their drawing, using the sound-spelling correspondences taught thus far.

Writing

Writing

Entering/Emerging
Have students use phrases and familiar vocabulary to describe their drawings.

Transitioning/Expanding
Have students describe their drawings using short sentence(s).

Bridging
Have students describe their drawings using longer, more detailed sentence(s).

Activity Page 5.1

Pausing Point

You should pause here and spend three days reviewing, reinforcing, or extending the material taught so far.

You may have students do any combination of the activities listed below, but it is highly recommended that you use the Mid-Domain Assessment to assess students' knowledge of *Seasons and Weather*. The other activities may be done in any order. You may also choose to do an activity with the whole class or with a small group of students who would benefit from the particular activity.

CORE CONTENT OBJECTIVES UP TO THIS PAUSING POINT

Students will:

- Demonstrate understanding of the following units of time and their relationship to one another: day, week, month, year

- Name the four seasons in cyclical order, as experienced in the United States, and correctly name a few characteristics of each season

- Characterize winter as generally the coldest season, summer as generally the warmest season, and spring and autumn as transitional seasons

- Draw pictures that show an understanding of each season

- Characterize the North and South Poles as always cold in temperature, the middle section of the earth as usually warm, and most of the United States as having four seasons

- Describe daily weather conditions of their own locality in terms of temperature (hot, warm, cool, cold), cloud cover (sunny, cloudy), and precipitation (rain, snow, sleet)

- Name at least one month in a specific season while referring to a calendar

- Name at least one holiday in a specific season

- Describe any unique seasonal differences that are characteristic of their own locality (change of color and dropping of leaves in autumn; snow or ice in winter; increased rain, and/or flooding in spring, etc.)

- Identify ways in which weather affects daily routines, such as dress, activities, etc.

- Identify a thermometer as an instrument used to measure temperature and describe how it works

Riddles for Core Content

Activity Page PP.1

Materials: Activity Page PP.1

Directions: I will read several riddles about the weather that name a characteristic of a certain season in most of the United States. Circle the image that stands for the season I describe. The snowflake stands for winter; the flower stands for spring; the sun stands for summer, and the leaf stands for autumn.

1. I am the season that has snowstorms called blizzards with very cold temperatures and lots of snow and wind. What season am I? *(winter)*

2. I am the season in which people go to swimming pools to keep cool. What season am I? *(summer)*

3. Young plants pop up out of the ground in this season. What season am I? *(spring)*

4. I am the season when leaves change colors and fall off some types of trees. What season am I? *(autumn)*

5. Some people celebrate Thanksgiving Day with turkey, pie, and football in this season. What season am I? *(autumn)*

6. I am the coldest season of the year. What season am I? *(winter)*

7. I am the season after winter when flowers bloom, plants grow, and baby animals are born. What season am I? *(spring)*

8. I am the hottest season of the year. What season am I? *(summer)*

ACTIVITIES

Domain-Related Trade Book or Student Choice

Materials: Trade Book

- Read a trade book to review a particular season; refer to the books listed in the Introduction at the front of this Teacher Guide. You may also choose to have students select a Read-Aloud to be heard again.

Image Card Review

Image Cards 1–5

Materials: Image Cards 1–5

- In your hand, hold Image Cards 1–5 fanned out like a deck of cards. Ask a student to choose a card but not show it to anyone else in the class. The student must then perform an action or give a clue about the picture they are holding. For example, for winter, a student may pretend to be shivering. The rest of the class will guess what is being described. Proceed to another card when the correct answer has been given.

Taking Temperatures: Water

Materials: Cups of warm, cool, and ice-cold water; thermometer; board or chart paper

- Place cups of warm, cool, and ice-cold water on a table. Take the temperature of each cup of water and show students the readings on the thermometer. Have students feel the water. Record the temperature of each cup on a chart. Ask students what they think will happen to the temperature of the water throughout the day. Later in the day, take the temperature of the water again. Have students feel the water again. Record the temperature of each cup on the chart. Ask students if their predictions were correct.

Holidays and Seasons

Materials: large monthly calendar; drawing paper, drawing tools

- Show students the monthly calendar. Ask students which holidays occur in each season. You may prompt students' responses by flipping through a large monthly calendar, calling out the names of the different months and reinforcing what months make up each season. Have students draw pictures of their favorite holidays. Help them to write at the top of their drawings the name of the holiday, and the month and season in which it occurs.

76

Knowledge 8   Seasons and Weather

Nouns and Verb Word Sort

Materials: List of nouns and verbs from the domain, additional common nouns and verbs; a set of two index cards for each student with the words "Thing or Noun" on one card and the word "Action or Verb" on the other.

- Distribute set of index cards to each student

- Review the meaning of each word on the cards. Remind students that nouns can mean a person, place or thing.

- Tell students that you will read a word to them and they will show if it is a thing or noun by holding up the "Thing or Noun" card.

- Tell them that they can show the word is an action word or verb by holding up the "Action or Verb" card.

- Read the words and wait for the card response before reading the next word on the list.

- If time allows, have students think of their own words and share orally with the class. Have the students use their cards to indicate if the word is a noun or a verb.

SEASONS AND WEATHER
The Grasshopper and the Ants

Speaking and Listening

Students will identify and describe characteristics of a fable.
[SL.K.4]

Reading

Students will discuss how seasons correspond to the main events in the story and will identify the moral in the fable.
[RL.K.9]

Language

Students will demonstrate an understanding of the Tier 2 word *last*.
[L.K.5c]

Writing

Students will sequence images to illustrate the cycle of seasons.
[W.K.2]

FORMATIVE ASSESSMENT

Activity Page 6.1

Cycle of the Seasons Students will sequence images to illustrate the cycle of seasons.
[W.K.2]

	Grouping	Time	Materials
Introducing the Read-Aloud			
What Have We Already Learned?	Whole Group	10 min	❏ calendar
			❏ world map
Essential Background Information or Terms			
Read-Aloud			
Purpose for Listening	Whole Group	30 min	
"The Grasshopper and the Ants"			
Comprehension Questions			
Word Work: *Last*			
This is a good opportunity to take a break.			
Application			
Syntactic Awareness Activity	Whole Group Independent	20 min	❏ Activity Page 6.1
			❏ Image Cards 2–5
			❏ scissors
Cycle of the Seasons			❏ glue or tape

ADVANCE PREPARATION

Introducing the Read-Aloud

• Be prepared to locate Greece on a world map.

Application

• Prepare to divide students into pairs for the Syntactic Awareness Activity.

Universal Access

• Bring in a copy of Aesop's fables for students to look at. Consider using the book as an example when you discuss the term *author* in Introducing the Read-Aloud.

future, n. a time that will happen later
Example: I have never visited Disney World, but I hope to go there in the future.
Variation(s): futures

last, v. to have enough of something for a certain period of time
Example: The holiday treats will last them through the month.
Variation(s): lasts, lasted, lasting

shivering, v. shaking from the cold; trembling
Example: Mary was shivering from the chill in the air, and wished she had worn her scarf.
Variation(s): shiver, shivers, shivered

Vocabulary Chart for "The Grasshopper and the Ants"			
Type	Tier 3 Domain-Specific Words	Tier 2 General Academic Words	Tier 1 Everyday Speech Words
Vocabulary		future (*futuro*) shivering	
Multiple Meaning		last	
Sayings and Phrases	hard at work paid no attention put away woke up		

Lesson 6: The Grasshopper and the Ants

Introducing the Read-Aloud

10ᴍ

Support

Have the class chant each month and corresponding season.

Speaking and Listening: Students will identify and describe characteristics of a fable.

[SL.K.4]

WHAT HAVE WE ALREADY LEARNED? (5 MIN)

- Have students identify in proper sequence the four seasons of the year in most of the United States.

- Remind students that their pen pal, Annie, has written them about all four seasons.

- Briefly review the characteristics of each season. As you discuss the months in each season, be sure to flip through your monthly calendar.

- Now tell students that they will not hear a letter from Annie today. Instead they will hear a story that is about different seasons of the year.

Speaking and Listening

Exchanging Information and Ideas

Entering/Emerging
Ask students yes/no questions about the fables and characters they have already read about.

ESSENTIAL BACKGROUND INFORMATION OR TERMS (5 MIN)

- Ask students if they remember any of the fables they heard earlier in the year.

- Have students list the fables and characters they remember from Domain 1, *Nursery Rhymes and Fables. (Answers may vary, but may include "The Lion and Mouse," "The Dog and His Reflection," and "The Hare and the Tortoise.")*

- Tell the class that there was a man named Aesop [/ee*sop/] who lived in Greece a very long time ago.

- Locate Greece for students on a world map.

- Ask them to say the name *Aesop*.

- Tell them that in Aesop's time, people did not have storybooks, so they told stories aloud to one another.

Transitioning/Expanding
Encourage students to build on what the previous students have said about fables.

Bridging
Challenge students to say something more about what the previous students have said about fables.

- Explain that Aesop was a great storyteller. He was known for collecting and retelling many short stories called fables.

- Explain that stories were passed down orally, or by word of mouth, from parents to children and from neighbor to neighbor for thousands of years.

- Tell students that stories today can still be passed down orally, although many stories are also written down and read in books.

- Explain that fables often have animals as characters in the story, instead of people.

- Remind students that when any animal or thing acts like a person in a story, the writing technique that the author is using is called personification. Have students say the word *personification*. Personification is when animals in a story talk and act like people do.

- Like all fables, Aesop's fables were intended to teach a lesson, called the moral of the story. Ask students to repeat the name *Aesop* once again. Then have them tell you what the lesson taught in a fable is called. *(The lesson taught in a fable is called the moral of the story.)*

Challenge

Ask students to identify and summarize the moral of a fable they remember from Domain 1.

Check for Understanding

Recall: What is an author? *(A person who writes a book.)*

What is the name of the Greek storyteller known for writing fables? *(Aesop is known for writing fables.)*

What is another name for the lesson of a story? *(Another name for the lesson of the story is the moral.)*

Lesson 6: The Grasshopper and the Ants
Read-Aloud

30M

Reading: Students will discuss how seasons correspond to the main events in the story and will describe the moral in the fable.
[RL.K.9]

Language: Students will demonstrate an understanding of the Tier 2 word *last*.
[L.K.5c]

PURPOSE FOR LISTENING

- Tell students that today they are going to hear the story of "The Grasshopper and the Ants," one of Aesop's many fables.

- Explain that this story takes place throughout the different seasons of the year.

- Tell them to listen carefully so they can identify the different seasons and learn what happens in the story.

- Have students also listen to find out what moral or lesson the grasshopper learns at the end of the fable.

"THE GRASSHOPPER AND THE ANTS" (15 MIN)

Show image 6A-1: Grasshopper and ants
[Have students identify the grasshopper and the ants in the image.]

In a field on a fine summer's day, a grasshopper was hopping about, singing and dancing and enjoying himself.

Nearby, a group of ants was hard at work. They had built their house underground, and they were filling it with food to **last** them through the long, cold winter ahead. *They were filling the house with lots of food during the summer, so that they would have enough to eat throughout the entire winter.*

Support

The word *last* also means end or final.

"Why not come and play with me?" asked the grasshopper. "Why bother about winter? We have plenty of food now. Come, leave your work. Now's the time to dance and sing."

But the ants paid no attention to the grasshopper. They kept working hard, all day and every day. *Why do you think the ants are working so hard?*

Speaking and Listening

Offering Opinions

Entering/Emerging
Provide students sentence frames using a small set of learned phrases (e.g., "The ants are working hard to prepare for winter.").

Transitioning/Expanding
Provide students sentence frames using an expanded set of learned phrases (e.g., "The ants should/should not work so hard.").

Bridging
Provide minimal support and guidance for open responses.

Show image 6A-2: The grasshopper napping under a tree
[Have students describe the grasshopper in this image.]

But not the grasshopper. All summer long, while the ants worked, he jumped about the field and danced and sang. Sometimes he'd sit for hours and listen to the humming of the bees, or watch the butterflies flitting about, or take long, lazy naps in the warm sun. And when he woke up, he would sing this song:

The summertime's the time for me,

For then I'm happy as can be.

I watch the butterflies and bees,

As they fly around as they please.

Oh, summertime's the time for me!

For I'm as happy as can be.

Yes, the grasshopper was a happy fellow—but he never thought about the **future**. *He never thought about what would happen later in time, in the future; he only thought about what was happening right now, in the present.*

Show image 6A-3: Grasshopper in late fall
One day the grasshopper woke up and felt a chill in the air. Then he saw the leaves turn red, gold, and brown, and fall from the trees. Then the days kept getting cooler, and soon, the grasshopper saw no butterflies or bees, and the fields where he liked to sing and dance

turned bare and hard. *Bare means not covered. The leaves fell off the trees and the grass in the fields died. What season of the year is it now?*

Soon, the cold days of winter were upon him, and the grasshopper was freezing and hungry. He came to the ants' house and knocked on the door.

Show image 6A-4: Grasshopper knocking at the ants' door
Why do you think the grasshopper is knocking at the ants' door?

"What do you want?" asked the ants.

"May I come in and share your food?" asked the grasshopper.

"What did you do all summer?" asked the ants. "Didn't you put away some food to use now?" *Didn't you save food during the summer to use now?*

"No," said the **shivering** grasshopper. *The word* shivering *means he was shaking from the cold. Show me what the grasshopper looked like when he was shivering. In what season do people tend to shiver?* "I didn't think of that while I was singing and dancing in the sun."

"So," said the ants meanly, "you sang and danced all summer while we worked. Well, now you can sing and dance while we eat!" *Was this a nice thing for the ants to say to the grasshopper? Would you have helped the grasshopper if you were the ants?*

And as the hungry grasshopper walked away, he sang this song:

Next time I'll work as well as dance,

Then I'll be ready, like the ants!

Check for Understanding

Recall: What is the season at the beginning of the fable? *(Summer is the season at the beginning of the fable.)*

What season comes after summer? *(Autumn is the season that comes after summer.)*

What is the season at the end of the fable? *(Winter is the season at the end of the fable.)*

What changes happen to the weather and the trees in autumn after summer ends? *(After summer ends, it becomes cold. The trees become bare and there is less food for the animals to eat.)*

COMPREHENSION QUESTIONS (10 MIN)

1. **Inferential** Describe the grasshopper at the beginning of the fable, during the summer. *(At the beginning of the fable in the summer, the grasshopper is playful and happy.)*

   ◦ **Inferential** Describe the ants during the summer. *(During the summer, the ants are hardworking and looking for food to save for the winter.)*

2. **Inferential** In the fable, who is thinking about what would happen later in time, in the future: the grasshopper or the ants? *(The ants are thinking about the future because they are saving food to eat during the winter.)*

3. **Inferential** What happened to the grasshopper at the end of the fable? *(The grasshopper was hungry and had no food at the end of the fable.)* Why? *(He didn't work hard like the ants, so he did not have any food saved to eat.)*

4. **Evaluative** What do you think the moral or lesson of the story is? *(You need to think ahead and prepare for the future.)*

   ◦ **Evaluative** Were the ants right to turn the grasshopper away? What would you have done? *(Answers may vary.)*

5. **Evaluative** *Think Pair Share:* Do you think what happens in this Read-Aloud could really happen, or is it pretend or fantasy? Why? *(The story is pretend or fantasy because animals cannot talk, sing, and dance like people. However, the lesson is real—it is important to think ahead and prepare for the future.)*

Support

If students have difficulty responding to questions, reread pertinent lines of the Read-Aloud and/or refer to specific images.

Challenge

Remind students that personification is when animals in a story talk like people do. Ask students when Aesop uses personification in this fable. *(Aesop uses personification when the grasshopper and ants talk and act like people in the story.).*

WORD WORK: LAST (5 MIN)

1. In the Read-Aloud you heard, "[A group of ants] had built their house underground, and they were filling it with food to last them through the long, cold winter ahead."

2. Say the word *last* with me.

3. The word *last* has many meanings. In this case, *last* means to have enough of something for a certain period of time.

4. A box of new crayons can last the school year, or a song can last five minutes.

5. Tell about something you know that can last for a certain amount of time, like a week or a day. Try to use the word *last* when you tell about it. [Ask two or three students. If necessary, guide and/or rephrase students' responses: "Something I know that can last a week is . . ." or "Something I know that can last a day is . . ."]

6. What's the word we've been talking about?

Use a Making Choices activity for follow-up. If any of the things I say can last, say, "_____ will last." If it cannot last, say, "_____ will not last."

- an ice cube on the sidewalk during the summer (*An ice cube on the sidewalk will not last during the summer.*)

- one can of cat food for the cat for the entire winter (*One can of cat food for the cat will not last for the entire winter.*)

- a new pair of shoes for a week (*A new pair of shoes will last for more than a week.*)

- two sheets of paper for the school year (*Two sheets of paper will not last for the school year.*)

- a video or DVD that I can watch many times (*A video or DVD that I can watch many times will last.*)

Lesson 6: The Grasshopper and the Ants
Application

20 M

Writing: Students will sequence images to illustrate the cycle of seasons.
[W.K.2]

SYNTACTIC AWARENESS ACTIVITY (5 MIN)

Asking and Answering Questions Using Who

- Tell students they are going to practice answering questions that use the question word *who*.

- Explain that we ask questions by using question words. When someone asks a question using the question word *who*, they are asking a question about people.

Show image 6B-1: Girls playing basketball

- Ask students to look at the following picture and answer the following question using a complete sentence:

  ◦ Who is playing basketball in this image? *(The girls are playing basketball.)*

  ◦ Which word in the question let you know that my question was about the people in the image? *(who)*

- Remind students that *who* is a question word used to ask questions about people.

Show image 6B-2: Summer activities

- Repeat this process for the three pictures in image 6B-2, explaining to students that *who* is a question word used to ask questions about people.

- Have students work with a partner to ask and answer a question using the word *who*.

CYCLE OF THE SEASONS (15 MIN)

- Have students name the set of months in each season as they occur in most of the United States, and have students identify the corresponding season.

- As they name the season, show the corresponding image card for the season: Image Card 2 (Winter); 3 (Spring); 4 (Summer); and 5 (Autumn).

- Have each student turn to Activity Page 6.1.

Flip Book 6B-1, 6B-2

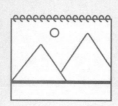

Support

Ask the students to repeat the question and answer after you.

Image Cards 2–5

Activity Page 6.1

- Ask students to listen carefully to your instructions before they start working.

- Have students cut along the dashed line directly above the season pictures.

- Next, have students cut out each season picture separately.

- Ask students to glue or tape each season picture in the correct box, beginning with the winter box labeled number one.

- Have students show their cycles to the class and say each season name as they progress through the correct sequence.

End Lesson

Writing

Writing

Entering/Emerging
Have students use phrases and familiar vocabulary to describe the cycle of seasons.

Transitioning/Expanding
Have students describe the cycle of seasons using short sentence(s).

Bridging
Have students describe the cycle of seasons using longer, more detailed sentence(s).

Challenge

Have students include a word, phrase, or sentence that describes their drawing, using the sound-spelling correspondences taught thus far.

7

SEASONS AND WEATHER
Safety in Storms

Speaking and Listening

Students will review different types of weather and discuss the concept of safety.
[SL.K.2]

Reading

Students will describe the characteristics of a thunderstorm and how to stay safe during dangerous weather.
[RI.K.3]

Language

Students will demonstrate an understanding of the Tier 2 word *severe*.
[L.K.5c]

Writing

Students will use a drawing activity to illustrate a thunderstorm and describe how to stay safe during dangerous weather.
[W.K.2]

FORMATIVE ASSESSMENT

Drawing Activity

Storm Safety Students will use drawing to describe how to stay safe during a thunderstorm.
[W.K.2]

	Grouping	Time	Materials
Introducing the Read-Aloud			
What Have We Already Learned?	Whole Group	10 min	
Essential Background Information or Terms			
Read-Aloud			
Purpose for Listening	Whole Group	30 min	
"Safety in Storms"			
Comprehension Questions			
Word Work: *Severe*			
This is a good opportunity to take a break.			
Application			
Weather Diary	Independent Partner	20 min	❑ Activity Page 1.1
Storm Safety Drawing Activity			❑ drawing tools
			❑ paper folded in half

ADVANCE PREPARATION

Application

- Return weather diaries to students.

- Fold a sheet of paper in half for each student to use during the storm safety drawing activity.

Universal Access

- Gather different books about storms to pass around the class. The school and local libraries may be good resources. Be sure to highlight books with diverse character representation and authorship.

gear, n. specific clothing or tools needed for a particular reason
   Example: Rain gear includes rubber boots and raincoats.
   Variation(s): none

severe, adj. very bad
   Example: The severe look on his face shows that he is angry.
   Variation(s): severer, severest

shelter, n. a place that offers protection from bad weather or danger
   Example: We took shelter indoors when it rained yesterday.
   Variation(s): shelters

strike, n. a sudden, sharp blow
   Example: A lightning strike could cause a fire.
   Variation(s): strikes

Vocabulary Chart for "Safety in Storms"			
Type	**Tier 3** **Domain-Specific Words**	**Tier 2** **General Academic Words**	**Tier 1** **Everyday Speech Words**
Vocabulary		severe	
Multiple Meaning		gear shelter strike	
Sayings and Phrases	bolt of lightning storm clouds zig-zags		

Lesson 7: Safety in Storms

Introducing the Read-Aloud

Speaking and Listening: Students will review different types of weather and discuss the concept of safety.

[SL.K.2]

WHAT HAVE WE ALREADY LEARNED? (5 MIN)

• Discuss with students the different types of weather they have learned about: sunny weather, cloudy weather, windy weather, rainy weather, and stormy weather.

• Talk with students about each type of weather and the activities that can be done inside or outside during each type of weather.

• Explain that when the weather is nice, people like to be outside. When the weather is not so nice, people tend to stay indoors where it is safe and dry.

ESSENTIAL BACKGROUND INFORMATION OR TERMS (5 MIN)

• Talk to students about the words *safe* and *safety*.

• Tell students that these words can mean being careful or protected from danger.

• Ask students what comes to mind when they think of the weather and the words *safe* and *safety*.

• Tell students you are going to name a type of weather that can be unpleasant or even dangerous. Say the word *thunderstorm*.

• Ask students what comes to mind when they think of thunderstorms. Have students share their ideas.

Speaking and Listening

Exchanging Information and Ideas

Entering/Emerging
Ask students yes/no questions about thunderstorms.

Transitioning/Expanding
Encourage students to build on what the previous student has said about thunderstorms.

Bridging
Challenge students to say something more about what the previous student has said about thunderstorms.

Support

Have students turn to a partner and use the words *safe* and *safety* in sentences.

Challenge

Have students discuss different types of storms using the words *safe* and *safety*.

Check for Understanding

Thumbs Up/Thumbs Down: Is it safe to cross the street without looking both ways? *(thumbs down)*

Is it safe to wear a helmet when riding a bike? *(thumbs up)*

Is it safe to go inside when there is a thunderstorm? *(thumbs up)*

Lesson 7: Safety in Storms
Read-Aloud

Reading: Students will describe the characteristics of a thunderstorm and how to stay safe during dangerous weather.
[RI.K.3]

Language: Students will demonstrate an understanding of the Tier 2 word *severe*.
[L.K.5c]

PURPOSE FOR LISTENING

- Tell students that in the Read-Aloud today, Annie will be talking about what you can do to stay safe during a thunderstorm.

- Tell students to listen carefully for what they should do next time they encounter stormy weather.

"SAFETY IN STORMS" (15 MIN)

Show image 7A-1: Storm clouds
[Have students describe what they see in the picture.]

Dear Kindergartners,

Have you ever seen a thunderstorm? I got caught in one the other day, and it made me realize just how amazing and powerful the weather can be! The thunder boomed and lightning flashed—it was quite a show. Today I'm going to tell you about **severe** *or very bad* weather, and how to stay safe during thunderstorms.

You probably know what kind of weather to expect when you look up and see large, dark clouds like these in the sky. These are storm clouds, and unless you want to get soaked, it's time to get indoors when you see a storm like this moving in. *The word* soaked *means to become completely wet from the rain.*

Show image 7A-2: Lightning
During a thunderstorm, you can see lightning. Lightning is a stroke of electricity that connects energy in the ground with energy in a cloud. Sometimes, you can see a bolt of lightning when it flashes and zig-zags in the sky.

Lightning is often followed by a loud clap of thunder. If the thunderstorm is far away, then the thunder may only sound like a distant rumble. But as the storm nears, the thunder gets louder and louder, and the time between the lightning and thunder gets shorter and shorter. Thunder cannot hurt you, but lightning can be dangerous.

Show image 7A-3: Lightning-struck tree
A lightning **strike** *or sudden sharp blow* knocked down this tree. Lightning can start fires, too. Worst of all, lightning can seriously injure, or hurt, a person. There is a very small chance of being struck by lightning, but it can happen. Fortunately, there are simple ways to be safe from lightning during a storm. My teachers taught them to me, and now I'm going to teach them to you.

Lightning tends to strike *or hit with a sudden blow* tall things like trees and tall buildings. The smartest thing you can do in a storm is stay indoors. If you can't take cover in a building, then a car is also a safe place.

In case you ever get stuck outside in a thunderstorm and you cannot get indoors, it is important that you remember never to take **shelter** *or look for protection* under or near a tree or tall object. Even though the tree leaves may help keep you dry, you never want to be near a tree if it gets hit by lightning. Instead, you should lie down flat on the ground, far away from any trees, and wait for the storm to pass—you'll get drenched, but you won't get struck by lightning or a falling tree. *The word* drenched *means to become completely wet from the rain.*

Another important rule is always to get out of a pool, lake, river, or ocean immediately during a thunderstorm. Electricity moves through water, so anyone in the water can be hurt by a single lightning strike. It's best to be safe and stay dry inside during a thunderstorm!

Challenge

Ask students which other word in this Read-Aloud means drenched. *(soaked)*

Show image 7A-4: Hail

When it is cold outside, you might see hail during a storm. During a hailstorm, chunks of ice, called hailstones, fall from the clouds onto the ground. Usually, hailstones are small—about the size of peas or smaller. Sometimes, however, hailstones can be as big as a golf ball or even a baseball. It is always best to stay indoors during a hailstorm.

Show image 7A-5: Annie in rain gear

It is important to know how to stay safe during storms and other kinds of severe weather. If possible, don't go outside at all in any kind of storm. If you have to go outside, wear the right kind of **gear**, *or specific type of clothing needed for a particular purpose* like a raincoat, boots, and a hat during rainstorms. Be smart and be safe, so you can enjoy the amazing power of nature. It's quite the show! Your friend,

Annie

Check for Understanding

Use Evidence: Describe some characteristics of a thunderstorm. *(Answers may vary, but may include that some characteristics of a thunderstorm are heavy rain, thunder, lightning, and strong winds.)*

COMPREHENSION QUESTIONS (10 MIN)

1. **Literal** What is lightning? (*Lightning is electricity that strikes the ground during a thunderstorm.*)

2. **Inferential** What should you do to stay safe during a thunderstorm? (*To stay safe during a thunderstorm, you should stay indoors or in a car, stay away from tall trees, and immediately get out of pools or other areas with lots of water.*)

3. **Literal** What are hailstones? (*Hailstones are chunks of ice that fall from the clouds during a storm.*)

4. **Literal** What gear, or special type of clothing, is best to wear if you have to go outside in the rain? (*If you have to go outside in the rain, it is best to wear a raincoat, boots, and a hat.*)

5. **Evaluative** *Think Pair Share:* Have you ever experienced a thunderstorm? What did you see? What did you hear? Try to use your five senses to describe it. (*Answers may vary, but should include support from the Read-Aloud.*)

WORD WORK: SEVERE (5 MIN)

1. In the Read-Aloud you heard, "Today I'm going to tell you about severe weather, and how to stay safe during thunderstorms."

2. Say the word *severe* with me.

3. *Severe* means very bad.

4. Someone's facial expression can be severe if they are very angry, or the weather can be severe if it is dangerous.

5. Tell about something you know that is severe. Try to use the word *severe* when you tell about it. [Ask two or three students. If necessary, guide and/or rephrase students' responses: "One thing I know that is severe is . . ."]

6. What's the word we've been talking about?

Use an Antonyms activity for follow-up. The opposite of *severe* is *gentle.* If any of the things I say sound severe, say, "_____ is severe." If any of the things sound gentle, say, "_____ is gentle."

- a kitten (*A kitten is gentle.*)
- blisters from a sunburn (*Blisters from a sunburn are severe.*)
- soft spring rain (*Soft spring rain is gentle.*)
- breaking an arm (*Breaking an arm is severe.*)
- snowflakes falling on your face (*Snowflakes falling on your face are gentle.*)

Lesson 7: Safety in Storms
Application

Writing: Students will use a drawing activity to illustrate a thunderstorm and describe how to stay safe during dangerous weather.

[W.K.2]

WEATHER DIARY (10 MIN)

- Have students turn to Activity Page 1.1.

- Have students observe the weather from a classroom window.

- Ask them to draw a simple picture of a sun, a sun with clouds, clouds, or clouds and rain depending on the weather each day.

- If you have an outside thermometer, you may also wish to have students write down the outside temperature, and/or have them draw a simple thermometer and color in how high or low the liquid in the thermometer is.

- Have students compare the weather observed yesterday and today.
  - What is the weather like today?
  - How is the weather today different from the weather yesterday?
  - What do you think the weather will be like tomorrow?

- Discuss the characteristics of the current season in your locality as well as the weather changes and temperature changes that occur.

- Help students identify any patterns that may have occurred over the five days they observed the weather.

- Tell students that they will be completing their Weather Diaries today.

- Tell students that they will need to create a title page for their diary. Show students an example of a title page.

- Lead a discussion about what information goes on a title page. Discuss the title, role of the author, and role of the illustrator.

Support

Have students work in pairs to decide what to draw.

Writing

Writing

Entering/Emerging
Have students use phrases and familiar vocabulary to describe facts and observations noted in their weather diaries.

Transitioning/Expanding
Have students share facts and observations from their weather diaries using short sentence(s).

Bridging
Have students share facts and observations from their weather diaries using longer, more detailed sentence(s).

Challenge

Have students label their diary entries with words, phrases, and sentences describing the weather they observed.

- Have students create title pages for the Weather Diaries, identifying themselves as the authors and illustrators. *(Note: the teacher could create a template and make copies for the title page that has "Weather Diary" the title and blanks next to "author" and "illustrator" so students can write in their own names.)*

- Collect the weather diaries to monitor progress. Be sure to return them to students for the next lessons.

STORM SAFETY DRAWING ACTIVITY (10 MIN)

- Give each student a sheet of paper folded in half.

- On one half of the paper, have students draw a picture of a thunderstorm using the information they have just heard in the Read-Aloud.

- On the second half of the paper, have students draw a picture of what a person should do to be safe in a thunderstorm.

- Have students turn to a partner to talk about their pictures.

- Tell students to suggest details their partner could add to the drawing.

- Return the papers to the original owners and allow students time to add details based on peer suggestions.

- Discuss with students how each person was able to add some new information to the original illustrations.

- Allow several volunteers to share and discuss their own and their partner's illustrations.

- As students discuss the illustrations, remember to repeat and expand upon each response using richer and more complex language, including, if possible, any Read-Aloud vocabulary.

~~~~~~~~~~~~~~~~~ End Lesson ~~~~~~~~~~~~~~~~~

Challenge

Have students label their drawings with words, phrases, and sentences describing the storm and what people can do to stay safe in dangerous weather.

SEASONS AND WEATHER
Meteorology

PRIMARY FOCUS OF LESSON

Speaking and Listening

Students will discuss the terms *meteorology* and *meteorologist* as well as the importance of predicting the weather.
[SL.K.1]

Reading

Students will identify key meteorological terms and describe why weather predictions are important.
[RI.K.3]

Language

Students will demonstrate an understanding of the Tier 2 word *warning*.
[L.K.5c]

Speaking and Listening

Students will use a writing activity to predict the weather and will orally present their predictions in a weather report.
[SL.K.5; W.K.1]

FORMATIVE ASSESSMENT

Activity Page 1.1

Weather Diary Students write about and present their weather predictions.
[SL.K.5; W.K.1]

	Grouping	Time	Materials
Introducing the Read-Aloud			
What Have We Already Learned?	Whole Group	10 min	
Essential Background Information or Terms			
Read-Aloud			
Purpose for Listening	Whole Group	30 min	
"Meteorology"			
Comprehension Questions			
Word Work: *Warning*			
This is a good opportunity to take a break.			
Application			
Weather Report	Independent	20 min	❑ Activity Page 1.1 ❑ drawing tools ❑ local map ❑ white board or chart paper

ADVANCE PREPARATION

Application

- Prepare a local map for students to use as they give their weather reports.

- If necessary, divide students into groups to give their weather reports.

Universal Access

- Show students video clips of meteorologists giving weather reports.

meteorologist, n. a person who studies and predicts the weather
Example: The meteorologist on the news predicts that it will snow
tomorrow.
Variation(s): meteorologists

meteorology, n. the study of weather and making weather predictions
Example: I learned about ice storms when I took a class on meteorology.
Variation(s): none

record, n. a written report of an event
Example: The weather record states that it rained a total of thirty inches
last year.
Variation(s): records

satellites, n. objects designed to go around Earth in space and collect
information
Example: The weather satellites recorded the hurricane's movements over
the Atlantic Ocean.
Variation(s): satellite

warning, v. telling someone in advance that danger is near
Example: The siren wailed, warning us that a tornado was nearby.
Variation(s): warn, warns, warned

	Vocabulary Chart for "Meteorology"		
Type	**Tier 3** **Domain-Specific Words**	**Tier 2** **General Academic Words**	**Tier 1** **Everyday Speech Words**
Vocabulary	meteorologist meteorology satellites	warning	
Multiple Meaning		record	
Sayings and Phrases	throw their way		

Offering Opinions

Entering/Emerging
Provide students sentence frames using a small set of learned phrases (e.g., "I liked learning about thunderstorms.").

Transitioning/Expanding
Provide students sentence frames using an expanded set of learned phrases (e.g., "I liked learning about thunderstorms because . . .").

Bridging
Provide minimal support and guidance for open responses.

Support

Have students say *meteorology*. Then, have them say *meteorologist*.

Lesson 8: Meteorology
Introducing the Read-Aloud

(10 M)

Speaking and Listening: Students will discuss the terms *meteorology* and *meteorologist* as well as the importance of predicting the weather.
[SL.K.1]

WHAT HAVE WE ALREADY LEARNED? (5 MIN)

- Remind students that their pen pal, Annie, has written them many letters about all four seasons.

- In the last Read-Aloud, Annie shared information about how to be safe during thunderstorms. Lead students in a discussion about safety tips during thunderstorms.

- Tell students that today, they will hear Annie's last letter about seasons and weather.

- Have students discuss what they have enjoyed learning about most from Annie.

ESSENTIAL BACKGROUND INFORMATION OR TERMS (5 MIN)

- Tell students that in today's letter, Annie will discuss the study of weather and predicting, or figuring out, what the weather will be like before it happens.

- Tell students that the words *meteorology* and *meteorologist* deal with weather and predicting weather.

- Explain to students that meteorology is the study of weather and weather prediction, and a meteorologist is a person who studies weather and predicts what the weather will be like before it happens.

- Have students discuss why being able to predict the weather for the day or for the week is important.

  ○ For example, they will need to know what the weather will be like on the weekend if they are going to an outdoor soccer game on Saturday.

- Encourage students to name ways in which weather is important to their everyday lives and how knowing the weather ahead of time will help them prepare for the day.
  - For example, hearing the weather report will help them know what to wear to school.

Check for Understanding

Stand Up/Sit Down: Meteorology is the study of plants. *(sit down)*

Meteorologists study and predict the weather. *(stand up)*

Knowing the weather predictions can help us plan our activities for the day. *(stand up)*

Challenge

Ask students to give examples of times when weather predictions helped them prepare for the day or encouraged them to change their plans for the day.

Lesson 8: Meteorology
Read-Aloud

(30ᴍ)

Reading: Students will identify key meteorological terms and describe why weather predictions are important.

[RI.K.3]

Language: Students will demonstrate an understanding of the Tier 2 word *warning*.

[L.K.5c]

PURPOSE FOR LISTENING

- Tell students to listen for the different types of people who depend on meteorologists' predictions of the weather.

"METEOROLOGY" (15 MIN)

Show image 8A-1: Annie writing

Dear Kindergartners,

This is my last letter to you about seasons and weather. Today we will learn how to know what kind of weather is on the way.

Show image 8A-2: Meteorologist

Have you ever watched the weatherman or weatherwoman on the news? Sometimes, people blame the weatherman for bad weather, especially when their plans are spoiled by rain. *Here,* spoiled *means ruined.* But the weatherman does not control the weather—he just tries to predict, or make his best guess at, what the weather is going to be like later in the day, tomorrow, or next week. Sometimes he is right, and sometimes he is wrong.

The study of weather and making weather predictions is called **meteorology**, and the person who does this is called a **meteorologist**. The words *weatherman* and *weatherwoman* are sometimes used to describe people who appear on television to tell you about the weather. Maybe you've seen them on the evening news. Often the weatherman or weatherwoman is a meteorologist.

Show image 8A-3: Family outdoors
[Have students describe the picture, concentrating on what the weather is like in the picture.]

Predicting weather is important so people will know what to wear that day and whether or not they will need an umbrella because of rain. Predicting weather also helps people to plan things like picnics or trips to the beach. If my parents are planning a family picnic, for example, they would want to make sure that it's not going to rain on us while we're outside!

Show image 8A-4: Farmer watering plants
But picnickers and vacationers are not the only ones who care what the meteorologist has to say. Farmers need to know how much rain to expect. If the meteorologist says it is not going to rain for a while, farmers may need to figure out another way to get water to their plants. In fact, anyone whose job could be affected by the weather needs a meteorologist, whether the person is a baseball player, a construction worker, a garbage man, an airline pilot, or an astronaut!

Show image 8A-5: Weather report
One way meteorologists predict what the weather will be like in the future is by studying weather patterns and temperatures from the past. When you watch a weather report, the weatherperson will tell you what the high, or warmest, temperature and the low, or coldest, temperature will be for that day. High temperatures usually come during the daytime and low temperatures are usually at night. However, the weatherperson can also tell you if the temperatures on a particular day are normal for that time of year by checking the weather **record** *or written report*. The weather record is kind of like a weather diary: it lists what the weather was like on that day in previous years. *Here, the word* record *means a written report of an event.*

Challenge

Have students discuss specific ways the weather can affect the people in the professions mentioned above.

Support

Tell students the word *record* can have other meanings. The word *record* also means a performance that is the best of its kind or an old-fashioned music disc.

Aside from looking at weather records, what else do meteorologists use to predict the weather? How do they know what is going to happen? In fact, predicting the weather is quite complicated, and even with all of the amazing computers and equipment we have nowadays, the weatherperson is still sometimes wrong.

Show image 8A-6: Satellite in orbit
However, meteorologists' predictions are also correct a lot of the time. This is thanks in part to **satellites** or objects designed to go around Earth in space and collect information like the one in this picture. *[Point to the satellite.]* Satellites are objects launched into space that contain cameras, radios, and antennas, but no people. Once in space, the satellites travel around the earth. The satellite cameras take pictures and beam them down to meteorologists. Using the photos, meteorologists can see storms as they develop and predict whether the skies will be clear or cloudy.

Show image 8A-7: Cumulus clouds
[Have students describe what they see in the picture.]

Of course, you don't always need a meteorologist to tell you what the weather is going to be like, especially if dark clouds like this roll over your town. These dark clouds are types of cumulus clouds and often develop into thunderstorms. You can also find cumulus clouds during nice weather, when they appear white and puffy like a cotton ball.

Show image 8A-8: Cirrus clouds
[Have students describe what they see in the picture.]

These are cirrus clouds. They are thin and wispy clouds that float way up high in the sky. Usually, cirrus clouds mean the weather is going to be clear and pleasant.

Show image 8A-9: Stratus clouds
[Have students describe what they see in the picture.]

Stratus clouds are the third cloud type, and they float fairly low to the ground. These flat clouds can stretch across the entire sky. They sometimes drop light rain or drizzle.

Show image 8A-10: Meteorologist studying hurricane

The most important part of a meteorologist's job is to help save lives by **warning** people *or telling people in advance* when severe weather is on the way. Look at this picture: it was taken when a hurricane was heading toward land. A hurricane is a huge storm that forms out over the ocean.

The meteorologist in this picture is studying images of a hurricane just as it is about to strike land. The image was made by a computer that is able—thanks to satellites, airplanes, and other tools—to determine how fast the wind is moving, how much it is raining, and in which direction the storm is moving.

Thanks to computers and satellites, the meteorologists saw the hurricane days before it came anywhere near land, so they warned people to leave their homes and head to safer ground if necessary. A lot of people were kept safe from this severe weather because of the meteorologists. Meteorologists help people stay prepared for and safe during whatever challenges the weather may throw their way.

Show image 8A-11: Annie says goodbye

Even though you can predict what the weather should be like during any given season where you live, it is difficult to always predict—from day to day—exactly what the weather will really be like. So, it is a good idea to listen to your local weatherman or weatherwoman, so you will know to carry an umbrella that day or bring along extra sunscreen. That way, you'll always be prepared.

Thank you so much for helping me with my weather project. From now on, I hope you'll keep an eye to the sky and always pay attention to the weather in your neighborhood!

Your friend,

Annie

Check for Understanding

Recall: What does a meteorologist do? (*A meteorologist studies and predicts the weather.*)

COMPREHENSION QUESTIONS (10 MIN)

1. **Inferential** Name some types of people who depend on meteorologists. (*Some types of people who depend on meteorologists are farmers, baseball players, and other people who work outside.*)

2. **Evaluative** If a meteorologist on the morning news show says it is going to rain today, how will that prediction affect your plans for the day? (*Rain will affect plans to spend time outdoors.*) For example, what will you wear? (*People wear a raincoat, rain boots, and a hat when it is raining.*)

3. **Literal** Describe how a weather satellite works. (*The satellite camera takes pictures of the weather on Earth. Then the satellite beams the pictures down to Earth.*)

4. **Inferential** What is one way you can tell what the weather will be like without listening to a meteorologist? (*You can tell what the weather will be like by looking at the clouds.*)

5. **Evaluative** *Think Pair Share:* The author said that predicting the weather is important. What are some examples the author gave for why it is important? (*Answers may vary, but should include evidence from the Read-Aloud.*) Why is predicting the weather important in your life? (*Answers may vary.*)

WORD WORK: WARNING (5 MIN)

1. In the Read-Aloud you heard, "The most important part of a meteorologist's job is to help save lives by warning people when severe weather is on the way."

2. Say the word *warning* with me.

3. *Warning* means telling someone in advance that danger is near. Other ways to say *warning* are warned or warns.

4. I help my little brother by warning him to look both ways when he crosses the street.

5. Is the word *warning* in that sentence a thing (noun) or an action word (verb)? (*It is an action, or verb*) Why? (*Answers may vary, but should include that the speaker is doing something, letting his brother know to look out when crossing the street.*)

6. Tell about something you are warning others not to do. Try to use the word *warning* when you tell about it. [Ask two or three students. If necessary, guide and/or rephrase students' responses: "I am warning you not to . . ."]

7. What's the word we've been talking about?

Support

If students have difficulty responding to questions, reread pertinent lines of the Read-Aloud and/or refer to specific images.

Speaking and Listening

Exchanging Information and Ideas

Entering/Emerging
Ask students yes/no questions about why predicting the weather is important.

Transitioning/Expanding
Encourage students to build on what the previous student has said about predicting the weather.

Bridging
Challenge students to say something more about what the previous student has said about predicting the weather.

Use a Making Choices activity for follow-up. If any of the things I say might be an example of warning someone of something, say, "_____ is warning someone." If any of the things I say is not an example of warning someone of something, say, "_____ is not warning someone."

- If you eat too much ice cream, you'll get a stomachache! *(That is warning someone.)*

- Come sit on the grass. It is soft. *(That is not warning someone.)*

- Don't go outside! It's raining! *(That is warning someone.)*

- What would you like for dinner? *(That is not warning someone.)*

- Come read with me. *(That is not warning someone.)*

Lesson 8: Meteorology
Application

Speaking and Listening: Students will use a writing activity to predict the weather and will orally present their predictions in a weather report.
[SL.K.5]

WEATHER REPORT (20 MIN)

- Tell students they are going to pretend to be a weatherperson on the news.

- Remind students that a weatherperson on the news is often a meteorologist.

Check for Understanding

Recall: What is a meteorologist? *(A meteorologist studies and predicts the weather.)*

- Tell students that they have been keeping track of the weather in their area and studying it, just like a meteorologist does.

- Have students turn to their weather diaries and read over the five entries they've made.

- Discuss the weather from the last few days and help students identify patterns that have occurred.

- Tell students that they will make a prediction based on their opinion of what the weather will be like tomorrow. Remind students that an opinion means that you have a feeling or idea about something. Remind students that they should make their prediction and give a reason to support why they think it will happen.

- Write the following on a white board or chart paper: "I predict that the weather tomorrow will be _____ because _____. "

- Have the students copy the sentence frame onto the last page of their weather diaries. Remind students to leave space to fill in the blanks.

Presenting

Presenting

Entering/Emerging
Read the student's prediction aloud to the class and allow the student to describe his/her illustration.

Transitioning/Expanding
Help the student prepare by reading the prediction aloud to them just before oral presentation.

Bridging
Have the student read their prediction aloud and describe their illustration independently in an oral presentation.

Challenge

Have students predict the weather for more than one day.

Support

Have students work in groups to come up with a prediction and present it to the class.

- Guide the students in filling in their prediction and their reason. Students will use their knowledge of phonetic spelling to write their words. Circulate while students are writing to provide support.

- Encourage students to predict things like temperature and rain fall.

- When sentences are complete, have students stand in front of the class to present their predictions like a weatherperson does on the news.

- Consider providing a map of your city or state for students to point to as they talk.

End Lesson

Domain Review

You should spend one day reviewing and reinforcing the material in this domain. You may have students do any combination of the activities provided, in either whole-group or small-group settings.

CORE CONTENT OBJECTIVES ADDRESSED IN THIS DOMAIN

Students will:

- Demonstrate understanding of the following units of time and their relationship to one another: day, week, month, year

- Name the four seasons in cyclical order, as experienced in the United States, and correctly name a few characteristics of each season

- Characterize winter as generally the coldest season, summer as generally the warmest season, and spring and autumn as transitional seasons

- Draw pictures that show an understanding of each season

- Characterize the North and South Poles as always cold in temperature, the middle section of the earth as usually warm, and most of the United States as having four seasons

- Describe daily weather conditions of their own locality in terms of temperature (hot, warm, cool, cold), cloud cover (sunny, cloudy), and precipitation (rain, snow, sleet)

- Name at least one month in a specific season while referring to a calendar

- Name at least one holiday in a specific season

- Describe any unique seasonal differences that are characteristic of their own locality (change of color and dropping of leaves in autumn; snow or ice in winter; increased rain, and/or flooding in spring, etc.)

- Identify ways in which weather affects daily routines, such as dress, activities, etc.

- Identify a thermometer as an instrument used to measure temperature and describe how it works

- Explain the lesson the grasshopper learns at the end of the fable, "The Grasshopper and the Ants"

- Identify characteristics of thunderstorms

- Describe safe and unsafe behaviors during thunderstorms

- Explain why weather prediction is important in daily life

REVIEW ACTIVITIES

My Active Season

Materials: Drawing paper, drawing tools

- Review with students the various activities that are common during each season. Ask students to draw themselves doing their favorite activities. Remind them to draw themselves dressed for the season. Help them to write the name of the activity and season on their papers.

Image Card Review

Materials: Image Cards 1–11

Image Cards 1–11

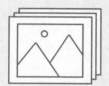

- In your hand, hold Image Cards 1–11 fanned out like a deck of cards. Ask a student to choose a card but not show it to anyone else in the class. The student must then perform an action or give a clue about the picture they are holding. For example, for cumulus clouds, a student may say, "white and puffy." The rest of the class will guess what is being described. Proceed to another card when the correct answer has been given.

Weather Safety Tips

- Review with students safety tips for thunderstorms. Review the word severe. Ask them if they have ever experienced a thunderstorm. Allow students to share their stories. Reinforce what they should do to be safe in these situations.

Key Vocabulary Brainstorming

Materials: Chart paper, chalkboard, or whiteboard

- Give students a key domain concept or vocabulary word such as clouds. Have students brainstorm everything that comes to mind when they hear the word, such as, "puffy, white," etc. Record their responses on the board or chart paper.

Riddles for Core Content

- To review core content, ask students riddles such as the following:

  - In the fable "The Grasshopper and the Ants," you heard that I spent my summer and autumn playing and singing instead of working. Who am I? *(the grasshopper)*

  - In the fable "The Grasshopper and the Ants," you heard that we worked hard all summer and autumn and, because of our hard work, had plenty of food for the winter. Who are we? *(the ants)*

  - I happen when it rains really, really hard and the ground and rivers cannot hold any more water. What am I? *(a flood)*

  - I am a refreshing summer activity that cools you off. What am I? *(swimming)*

  - Sometimes I strike tall things like trees and tall buildings. What am I? *(lightning)*

  - You should never take shelter under me during a thunderstorm. What am I? *(a tree)*

  - I study weather and give you my best prediction. What am I? *(a meteorologist)*

On Stage

- Choose students to act out the characters while you read "The Grasshopper and the Ants." Ask students what the moral of the story is. Ask students if they have ever chosen to play when they were supposed to work, and if so, what happened. If time allows, switch characters and read the story again, allowing students to dance while you sing or say the grasshopper's songs.

Rain Gauge

Materials: Clear bottle; funnel; ruler; tape

- Have students create a simple rain gauge using a clear bottle, a funnel, and a ruler. Tape the ruler to the side of the bottle and place the funnel in the mouth of the bottle. Place the rain gauge outside so that students can measure the amount of rain that falls in one week. Have students check the rain gauge daily and record the daily rainfall in their weather diaries.

Where is the Wind?

Materials: Grass or balloon; construction paper; scissors; tape; string

- Review with students what happens when the weather is windy. Take students outside on a windy day to learn more about the wind. Tell students that they can tell a lot about the wind, just by wetting their fingers and holding them up in the air. Have students discuss what they feel and which way they think the wind is blowing. Now have students confirm the direction of the wind by throwing grass or a balloon into the air. Discuss with students if their predictions about wind direction were correct.

- Students can also create a wind snake in order to make observations about the wind. Draw and cut a spiral on a piece of construction paper. Tape a piece of string to the middle of the snake and have students observe what happens to the snake when they hold it in the wind.

Domain Assessment

This domain assessment evaluates each student's retention of domain and academic vocabulary words and the core content targeted in *Seasons and Weather*. The results should guide review and remediation the following day.

There are three parts to this assessment. You may choose to do the parts in more than one sitting if you feel this is more appropriate for your students. Part I (Vocabulary Assessment) is divided into two sections: the first assesses domain-related vocabulary and the second assesses academic vocabulary. Parts II and III of the assessment address the core content targeted in *Seasons and Weather*.

PART I

Directions: I am going to ask a question using a word you have heard in the Read-Alouds. First I will say the word and then use it in a question. If the answer to the question is "yes," circle thumbs up. If the answer to the question is "no," circle thumbs down. I will ask each question two times. Let's do number one together.

Activity Page DA.1

1. **Seasons:** Are the four seasons called winter, spring, summer, and autumn? *(thumbs up)*

2. **Weather:** Does weather mean the temperature for the day and whether it is sunny, rainy, or cloudy? *(thumbs up)*

3. **Blizzards:** Do blizzards usually happen in the summer? *(thumbs down)*

4. **Freezing Point:** Is the freezing point the temperature at which water freezes? *(thumbs up)*

5. **Frigid:** When the weather is frigid outside, should we wear shorts? *(thumbs down)*

6. **Sunscreen**: Do we usually use sunscreen in the winter? *(thumbs down)*

7. **Floods**: Do floods occur when it rains really, really hard and the rivers cannot hold any more water? *(thumbs up)*

8. **Thermometer**: When we want to know the temperature outside, should we check the thermometer? *(thumbs up)*

9. **Meteorologist**: Is a meteorologist someone who studies weather? *(thumbs up)*

10. **Satellites**: Do satellites help scientists see storms as they develop and predict whether the skies will be clear or cloudy? *(thumbs up)*

Directions: Now I am going to ask more questions using other words you have heard in the Read-Alouds. First I will say the word and then use it in a question. If the answer to the question is "yes," circle thumbs up. If the answer to the question is "no," circle thumbs down. I will ask each question two times.

11. **Characteristics**: Do some characteristics of winter include that it snows and is often cold? *(thumbs up)*

12. **Cycle**: When something happens over and over again in the same order is it called a cycle? *(thumbs up)*

13. **Patterns**: Are patterns things that only happen once? *(thumbs down)*

14. **Gradually**: When something happens gradually, does it happen very, very quickly? *(thumbs down)*

15. **Severe**: Are thunderstorms a type of severe weather? *(thumbs up)*

PART II

Activity Page DA.2

Directions: I am going to name characteristics of a certain season in most of the United States. Circle the season I am describing on your paper. The snowflake stands for winter, the flower stands for spring, the sun stands for summer, and the leaf stands for autumn. Draw a picture of the current season on the back of the paper when you are finished.

1. During this season, the weather is very cold and it can even snow. *(winter)*

2. This is usually the hottest season of the year. *(summer)*

3. This is the season for farmers to plant seeds. *(spring)*

4. This is the season when leaves change colors and fall off trees. *(autumn)*

5. I would wear boots, a coat, mittens, a scarf, and a hat to go outside and play in this season. *(winter)*

6. The phrase, "April showers bring May flowers," is about what season? (spring)

7. This is the season for farmers to gather fruits and vegetables from their fields. *(autumn)*

PART III

Directions: I am going to read some questions to you. If the answer to the question is "yes," circle thumbs up. If the answer to the question is "no," circle thumbs down. I will ask each question two times.

1. Do meteorologists study the weather so they can predict what the weather will be like? *(thumbs up)*

2. If you hear thunder, should you go outside to play? *(thumbs down)*

3. During a thunderstorm, should you sit near a window? *(thumbs down)*

4. When you see lightning in the sky, should you stay away from trees and tall objects? *(thumbs up)*

5. Should you wear a jacket to go to a swimming pool in the summer? *(thumbs down)*

6. When it is hot outside, is the liquid in a thermometer high and nearer to the top? *(thumbs up)*

7. When it is cold outside, is the liquid in a thermometer low and nearer to the bottom? *(thumbs up)*

8. Do we celebrate the Fourth of July during summer? *(thumbs up)*

9. Is it sunny outside during a thunderstorm? *(thumbs down)*

10. Is a month shorter than a year? *(thumbs up)*

Culminating Activities

Please use these final two days to address class results of the Domain Assessment. Based on the results of the Domain Assessment scores, you may wish to use this class time to provide remediation opportunities that target specific areas of weakness for individual students, small groups, or the whole class.

Alternatively, you may also choose to use this class time to extend or enrich students' experience with domain knowledge. A number of enrichment activities are provided below in order to provide students with opportunities to enliven their experiences with domain concepts.

REMEDIATION

You may choose to regroup students according to particular areas of weakness, as indicated by Formative and Domain Assessments.

Remediation opportunities include:

• targeting Review Activities

• revisiting lesson Applications

• rereading and discussing select Read-Alouds

• reading the corresponding lesson in the Language Studio

ENRICHMENT

Cotton Clouds

Image Cards 7–9

Materials: Image Cards 7 (Cumulus Clouds), 8 (Cirrus Clouds), and 9 (Stratus Clouds); cotton balls, blue construction paper; glue, paint

• Using Image Cards 7–9, review the three types of clouds students learned: cumulus, cirrus, and stratus. Show students the image cards, and remind them of the different characteristics the different types of clouds have (e.g., cumulus clouds can be dark and stormy or white and puffy). Have students create their own pictures using cotton balls for clouds. Help them to pull apart and shape the cotton balls to represent the type of clouds they choose. If the clouds are stormy, have students lightly paint the cotton balls a dark color.

On Stage

- Choose students to act out the characters while you read "The Grasshopper and the Ants." Ask students what the moral of the story is. Ask students if they have ever chosen to play when they were supposed to work, and if so, what happened. If time allows, switch characters and read the story again, allowing students to dance while you sing or say the grasshopper's songs.

Severe Weather Drill

- Take some time to review your school's procedures for events of severe weather, such as a tornado drill. You may choose to practice a drill as a class. Tell students that you are going to practice what to do in the event that a tornado or hurricane hits while students are in school. Discuss safety procedures for severe weather. Explain that practicing what to do before a tornado or a hurricane hits will help the school be more prepared to take care of its students.

Meteorologist at Work

Materials: Video clip of the morning's weather report; board or chart paper

- Show students a clip of a meteorologist giving a weather report for the current day. Tell students that often people watch the weather report to know how to dress or be prepared for the day. Record on the board or chart paper, the predicted high and low temperatures of the day. Have students predict whether the highs and lows will be accurate. Check the temperature throughout the day and record it on chart paper, a chalkboard, or a whiteboard. Compare the weather report with the actual temperatures. Ask students when the highest and lowest temperatures occurred. Tell them to check with their parents tonight to see how low the temperatures go.

Tornado in a Bottle

Materials: Clear glass or plastic jar with lid; dish soap; glitter

- Tell students that a tornado is an enormous wind funnel that can occur in certain parts of the United States. Tell students that they can create a wind funnel using a jar and dish soap. You may also wish to add glitter for effect. Fill the jar with water and add one or two drops of dish soap to the jar of water. Hold the jar upright and shake in a circular motion to create a wind funnel, similar to the wind funnels created by tornadoes during certain types of thunderstorms. Have students discuss what they observe.

Cloud Observation

Materials: Window; plastic wrap; markers; clear tape

- Tell students that clouds are always moving in the sky, even when it is hard to see them move. Stretch plastic wrap over a window in your classroom and secure it with clear tape. Have students choose one marker color to trace the clouds in the morning, another marker color to trace the clouds mid-morning, and a third marker color to trace the clouds in the afternoon. Discuss with students what they observe about the clouds' movement: did the clouds stay in one place? Did they move slowly or quickly?

Class Book: Seasons and Weather

Materials: Drawing paper, drawing tools

- Tell the class or a group of students that they are going to create a class book to help them remember what they have learned in this domain. Have students brainstorm important information about the four seasons, weather prediction, and "The Grasshopper and the Ants." Have each student choose one idea to draw a picture of, and ask them to write a caption for the picture. Bind the pages to make a book to put in the class library for students to read again and again.

Teacher Resources

Kindergarten	Knowledge 8

Teacher Guide

Teacher Resources

In this section you will find:

- Activity Book Answer Key

ACTIVITY BOOK ANSWER KEY

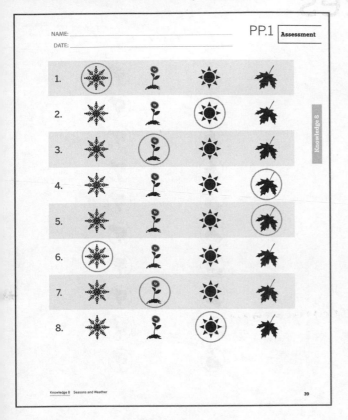

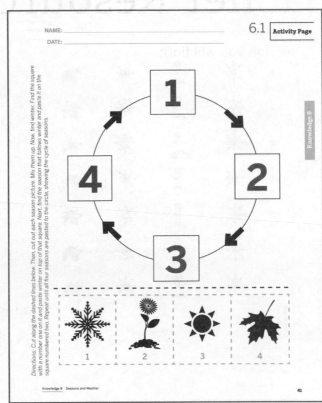

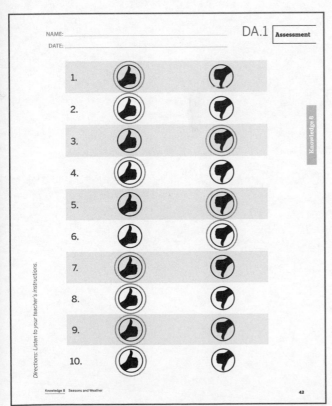

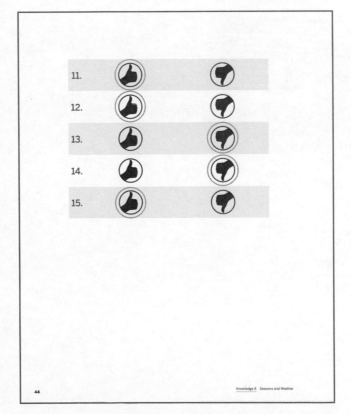

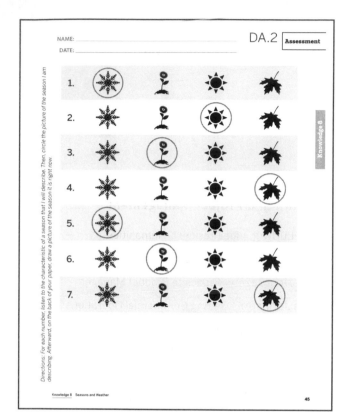

Directions: For each number, listen to the characteristic of a season that I will describe. Then, circle the picture of the season I am describing. Afterward, on the back of your paper, draw a picture of the season it is right now.

Knowledge 8

Knowledge 8 Seasons and Weather

45

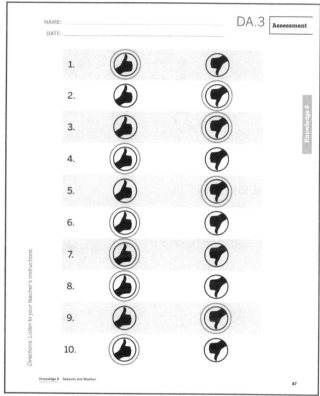

Directions: Listen to your teacher's instructions.

Knowledge 8

Knowledge 8 Seasons and Weather

47

Core Knowledge Language Arts
Amplify

Senior Vice President and General Manager, K-8 Humanities

LaShon Ormond

Chief Product Officer

Alexandra Walsh

Chief Academic Officer

Susan Lambert

Content and Editorial

Elizabeth Wade, PhD, Vice President, Editorial

Genya Devoe, Executive Director

Patricia Erno, Associate Director

Maria Oralia Martinez, Associate Director

Baria Jennings, EdD, Senior Content Developer

Sean McBride, Content and Instructional Specialist

Arysteja Szymanski, Content and Instructional Specialist

Mabel Zardus, Content and Instructional Specialist

Christina Cox, Managing Editor

Design and Production

Tory Novikova, Senior Director, Product Design

Erin O'Donnell, Director, Product Design

Julie Kim, Senior Product Design Manager

Ian Horst, Product Design Manager

Max Reinhardsen, Product Design Manager

Tara Pajouhesh, Senior Visual Designer

Product and Project Management

Nishi Ludwig, Vice President, Humanities

Amber Ely, Director, Product

Katherine Bazley, Associate Product Manager

Leslie Johnson, Director, Commercial Operations

Millie Triana, Operations Specialist

Melissa Cherian, Executive Director, Strategic Projects

Catherine Alexander, Associate Director, Project Management

Stephanie Melinger, Senior Project Manager

Zara Chaudhury, Project Manager

Patricia Beam Portney, Project Coordinator

Tamara Morris, Project Coordinator

Contributors

Cletis Allen, Nanyamka Anderson, Raghav Arumugan, Rosalie Asia, Dani Aviles, Olioli Buika, Bill Cheng, Sherry Choi, Stuart Dalgo, Claire Dorfman, Angelica Escalante, Edel Ferri, Rebecca Figueroa, Nicole Galuszka, Rodrigo Garcia, Parker-Nia Gordon, Danae Grandison, Ken Harney, Elisabeth Hartman, Molly Hensley, David Herubin, Isabel Hetrick, Sara Hunt, Sarah Kanu, Ashna Kapadia, Jagriti Khirwar, Kristen Kirchner, James Mendez-Hodes, Emily Mendoza, Francine Mensah, Christopher Miller, Lisa McGarry, Marguerite Oerlemans, Lucas De Oliveira, Melisa Osorio Bonifaz, Emmely Pierre-Louis, Jackie Pierson, Sheri Pineault, Diana Projansky, Dominique Ramsey, Todd Rawson, Darby Raymond-Overstreet, Max Reinhardsen, Jessica Roodvoets, Mia Saine, Zahra Sajwani, Natalie Santos, Meena Sharma, Jennifer Skelley, Nicole Stahl, Julia Sverchuk, Flore Thevoux, Elizabeth Thiers, Jeanne Thornton, Amanda Tolentino, Julie Vantrease, Paige Womack, Amy Xu, Jules Zuckerberg

Amplify CKLA

Core Knowledge Language Arts
Core Knowledge Foundation

Series Editor-in-Chief

E. D. Hirsch Jr.

President

Linda Bevilacqua

Editorial Staff

Mick Anderson
Robin Blackshire
Laura Drummond
Emma Earnst
Lucinda Ewing
Sara Hunt
Rosie McCormick
Cynthia Peng
Liz Pettit
Tonya Ronayne
Deborah Samley
Kate Stephenson
Elizabeth Wafler
James Walsh
Sarah Zelinke

Design and Graphics Staff

Kelsie Harman
Liz Loewenstein
Bridget Moriarty
Lauren Pack

Consulting Project Management Services

ScribeConcepts.com

Additional Consulting Services

Erin Kist
Carolyn Pinkerton
Scott Ritchie
Kelina Summers

Acknowledgments

These materials are the result of the work, advice, and encouragement of numerous individuals over many years. Some of those singled out here already know the depth of our gratitude; others may be surprised to find themselves thanked publicly for help they gave quietly and generously for the sake of the enterprise alone. To helpers named and unnamed we are deeply grateful.

Contributors to Earlier Versions of These Materials

Susan B. Albaugh, Kazuko Ashizawa, Kim Berrall, Ang Blanchette, Nancy Braier, Maggie Buchanan, Paula Coyner, Kathryn M. Cummings, Michelle De Groot, Michael Donegan, Diana Espinal, Mary E. Forbes, Michael L. Ford, Sue Fulton, Carolyn Gosse, Dorrit Green, Liza Greene, Ted Hirsch, Danielle Knecht, James K. Lee, Matt Leech, Diane Henry Leipzig, Robin Luecke, Martha G. Mack, Liana Mahoney, Isabel McLean, Steve Morrison, Juliane K. Munson, Elizabeth B. Rasmussen, Ellen Sadler, Rachael L. Shaw, Sivan B. Sherman, Diane Auger Smith, Laura Tortorelli, Khara Turnbull, Miriam E. Vidaver, Michelle L. Warner, Catherine S. Whittington, Jeannette A. Williams.

We would like to extend special recognition to Program Directors Matthew Davis and Souzanne Wright, who were instrumental in the early development of this program.

Schools

We are truly grateful to the teachers, students, and administrators of the following schools for their willingness to field-test these materials and for their invaluable advice: Capitol View Elementary, Challenge Foundation Academy (IN), Community Academy Public Charter School, Lake Lure Classical Academy, Lepanto Elementary School, New Holland Core Knowledge Academy, Paramount School of Excellence, Pioneer Challenge Foundation Academy, PS 26R (the Carteret School), PS 30X (Wilton School), PS 50X (Clara Barton School), PS 96Q, PS 102X (Joseph O. Loretan), PS 104Q (the Bays Water), PS 214K (Michael Friedsam), PS 223Q (Lyndon B. Johnson School), PS 308K (Clara Cardwell), PS 333Q (Goldie Maple Academy), Sequoyah Elementary School, South Shore Charter Public School, Spartanburg Charter School, Steed Elementary School, Thomas Jefferson Classical Academy, Three Oaks Elementary, West Manor Elementary.

And a special thanks to the CKLA Pilot Coordinators, Anita Henderson, Yasmin Lugo-Hernandez, and Susan Smith, whose suggestions and day-to-day support to teachers using these materials in their classrooms were critical.

Credits

Every effort has been taken to trace and acknowledge copyrights. The editors tender their apologies for any accidental infringement where copyright has proved untraceable. They would be pleased to insert the appropriate acknowledgment in any subsequent edition of this publication. Trademarks and trade names are shown in this publication for illustrative purposes only and are the property of their respective owners. The references to trademarks and trade names given herein do not affect their validity.

All photographs are used under license from Shutterstock, Inc. unless otherwise noted.

Expert Reviewer

Scott Curtis

Writer

Michael L. Ford

Illustrators and Image Sources

Cover: Steve Morrison; Title Page: Steve Morrison; Domain Icon: Core Knowledge Staff; Take Home Icon: Core Knowledge Staff; Cover: Steve Morrison; Title Page: Steve Morrison; 1A-1: Dustin Mackay; 1A-2 (top left): Shutterstock; 1A-2 (middle left): Shutterstock; 1A-2 (bottom left): Shutterstock; 1A-2 (right): Shutterstock; 1A-3 : Core Knowledge Staff; 1A-4: Shutterstock; 1A-5: Core Knowledge Staff; 1A-6: Shutterstock; 1A-7: Core Knowledge Staff; 1A-8 (top left): Shutterstock; 1A-8 (top right): Shutterstock; 1A-8 (bottom left): Shutterstock; 1A-8 (botton right): Shutterstock; 1A-9: Shutterstock; 1A-10: Shutterstock; 1A-11: Shutterstock; 1A-12: Shutterstock; 1A-13: Dustin Mackay; 2A-1: Dustin Mackay; 2A-2 (left): Core Knowledge Staff; 2A-2 (right): Core Knowledge Staff; 2A-3 (left): Shutterstock; 2A-3 (middle): Shutterstock; 2A-3 (right): Shutterstock; 2A-4: Shutterstock; 2A-5: Shutterstock; 2A-6: Shutterstock; 2A-7: Shutterstock; 2A-8: Shutterstock; 2A-9: Shutterstock; 2A-10 (top left): Shutterstock; 2A-10 (bottom left): Shutterstock; 2A-10 (right): Shutterstock; 2A-11: Dustin Mackay; 2A-12 (top left): Shutterstock; 2A-12 (top right): Shutterstock; 2A-12 (bottom left): Shutterstock; 2A-12 (bottom right): Shutterstock; 3A-1: Dustin Mackay; 3A-2: Dustin Mackay; 3A-3: Shutterstock; 3A-4: Shutterstock; 3A-5 (top left): Shutterstock; 3A-5 (top right): Shutterstock; 3A-5 (bottom): Shutterstock; 3A-6: Shutterstock; 3A-7 (top left): Shutterstock; 3A-7 (top right): Shutterstock; 3A-7 (bottom): Shutterstock; 3A-8: Shutterstock; 3A-9: Dustin Mackay; 4A-1 (top left): Shutterstock; 4A-1 (top right): Shutterstock; 4A-1 (bottom left): Shutterstock; 4A-1 (bottom right): Shutterstock; 4A-2: Dustin Mackay; 4A-3 (left): Core Knowledge Staff; 4A-3 (right): Core Knowledge Staff; 4A-4 (top left): Shutterstock; 4A-4 (top middle): Shutterstock; 4A-4 (top right): Shutterstock; 4A-4 (bottom left): Shutterstock; 4A-4 (bottom middle): Shutterstock; 4A-4 (bottom right): Shutterstock; 4A-5: Shutterstock; 4A-6: Shutterstock; 4A-7 (left): Core Knowledge Staff; 4A-7 (right): Core Knowledge Staff; 4A-8: Shutterstock; 4A-9: Shutterstock; 4A-10: Shutterstock; 4A-11: Shutterstock; 5A-1: Dustin Mackay; 5A-2: Shutterstock; 5A-3: Shutterstock; 5A-4: Shutterstock; 5A-5: Shutterstock; 5A-6: Shutterstock; 5A-7: Shutterstock; 5A-8: Shutterstock; 5A-9: Dustin Mackay; 5A-10: Shutterstock; 5A-11: Dustin Mackay; 6A-1: Steve Morrison; 6A-2: Steve Morrison; 6A-3: Steve Morrison; 6A-4: Steve Morrison; 6B-1: Shutterstock; 6B-2 (top left): Shutterstock; 6B-2 (bottom left): Shutterstock; 6B-2 (right): Shutterstock; 7A-1: Shutterstock; 7A-2: Shutterstock; 7A-3: Shutterstock; 7A-4 (left): Shutterstock; 7A-4 (right): Shutterstock; 7A-5: Dustin Mackay; 8A-1: Dustin Mackay; 8A-2 (man): Shutterstock; 8A-2 (map): Core Knowledge Staff; 8A-3: Dustin Mackay; 8A-4: Shutterstock; 8A-5: Core Knowledge Staff; 8A-6: Shutterstock; 8A-7 (left): Shutterstock; 8A-7 (right): Shutterstock; 8A-8: Shutterstock; 8A-9: Shutterstock; 8A-10: Shutterstock; 8A-11: Dustin Mackay; 38 (snowflake): Core Knowledge Staff; 38 (flower): Core Knowledge Staff; 38 (sun): Core Knowledge Staff; 38 (leaf): Core Knowledge Staff; 1B-1: Steve Morrison; 2B-1: Core Knowledge Staff; 3B-1: Core Knowledge Staff; 4B-1: Core Knowledge Staff; 5B-1: Core Knowledge Staff; PP-1: Core Knowledge Staff; PP-1 (Answer Key): Core Knowledge Staff; 6B-1: Core Knowledge Staff; 6B-1 (Answer Key): Core Knowledge Staff; DA-2: Core Knowledge Staff; DA-2 (Answer Key): Core Knowledge Staff

Regarding the Shutterstock items listed above, please note: "No person or entity shall falsely represent, expressly or by way of reasonable implication, that the content herein was created by that person or entity, or any person other than the copyright holder(s) of that content."